A comme

"Construction contracts"

Part II of the Housing Grants, Construction and Regeneration Act 1996

Raymond Joyce FICE Solicitor

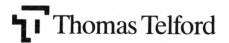

Thomas Telford

Published by Thomas Telford Publishing, Thomas Telford Services Ltd, 1 Heron Quay, London E14 4JD

First published 1996

Distributors for Thomas Telford books are
USA: American Society of Civil Engineers, Publications Sales Department, 345 East 47th Street, New York, NY 10017-2398
Japan: Maruzen Co. Ltd, Book Department, 310 Nihonbashi 2-chome, Chuo-ku, Tokyo 103
Australia: DA Books and Journals, 648 Whitehorse Road, Mitcham 3132, Victoria

A catalogue record for this book is available from the British Library

ISBN: 0 7277 2579 3

Typeset by Thomas Telford Publishing, London
Printed in Great Britain by Galliard (Printers) Ltd, Great Yarmouth, Norfolk

Preface

Part II of the Housing Grants, Construction and Regeneration Act 1996 ("the Act") deals solely with construction contracts. There has never been any previous legislation that seeks to regulate agreements entered into by parties to construction projects. This radical interventionist legislation could not be ignored by any self-respecting construction lawyer, nor should it be ignored by any other person with responsibility for negotiating or administering construction contracts.

This book is based on the preparation I undertook for a series of business briefings to the clients of Garrett & Co. The original business briefings, and therefore this book, were intended to be a practical guide for those responsible for negotiating, drafting and administering construction contracts.

The Act raises many questions, the answers to which cannot be predicted with any certainty. However, what I hope to have achieved is a critical review which familiarises the reader with the main provisions and identifies some of the difficult issues to be addressed in readiness for when Part II of the Act is fully in force.

The consultation process for the Scheme for Construction Contracts has just commenced with the intention that the Scheme will be finalised before mid-1997. Until such time as the Scheme is approved by both Houses of Parliament, Part II of the Act will not be in force.

When the Act received royal assent on 24 July 1996, John Gummer the Secretary of State for the Environment said:

> *"The legislation will underpin the moves of the construction industry to make itself more competitive in an increasingly international market."*

For the time being, the jury is out.

REJ, November 1996

Acknowledgements

I am grateful to the Official Referees Solicitors Association for its kind permission to reproduce its adjudication rules.

Writing a book is not a solitary occupation. In the first place there is the effort of motivation and the constant need for encouragement for which I am indebted to Steven Temblett of Thomas Telford Publishing. Secondly, there is a need to discuss and test my ideas and views with others. There are too many individuals to mention who have helped me to refine my ideas but special thanks are appropriate for my colleagues at Garrett & Co, particularly Adrian Watson, and also my brother, Stephen Joyce ARICS. My tapes and notes had to be typed, a task undertaken by my secretary, Cathrine Hill, who also provided her own comments and contribution to editing: for that a big thank you is due. Last, but not least, is the proof reading and critical review undertaken by my wife, Yvonne, to whom I am eternally indebted; but for her support and encouragement this book would never have been written.

The author

Raymond Joyce is head of construction and engineering law with Garrett & Co, where he specialises in all aspects of construction law. He spent the first 15 years of his career as a civil engineer before training as a solicitor and joining a leading firm of solicitors. He has been chairman of the Institution of Civil Engineers' Midlands Association and is active in Institution affairs.

GARRETT & CO

Garrett & Co specialises in UK business law for companies and organisations based in the UK and overseas. The clients of the firm benefit from partner intensive, cost effective services more usually associated with a small firm, together with a depth and breadth of experience provided by lawyers recruited from major practices. The firm, which has formed a unique association with Arthur Andersen through its membership of the Arthur Andersen international network of law firms, can give its clients access to an organisation with offices in 72 countries around the world; the resources to advise on complicated, time sensitive transactions; and access to the latest international company research and global economic and legal information.

Contents

Table of UK statutes

Table of statutory instruments

1 Introduction

Will construction contracts ever be the same again after the Housing Grants, Construction and Regeneration Act 1996 received royal assent on 24 July 1996? The answer is surely "no". However, the intention of the Act is not simply to tinker with clauses dealing with rights, duties and obligations of parties to a construction contract, but to bring about a fundamental change in the manner in which construction projects will be administered and managed.

Studies of the way in which the construction industry manages itself have been the subject of reports by Banwell in 1964[1] and Simon in 1944.[2]

It would not be unduly harsh to conclude that these studies, despite the good intentions of the authors, have made very effective book-ends to the large number of other books devoted to attempting to unravel the mystical meaning of construction contracts and different techniques of claims management and dispute resolution.

The perceived ills of the construction industry were soon forgotten in the boom of the late 1980s when there was sufficient work for all concerned. The inevitable bust brought with it a revisiting of unpredictable cash flow, insolvencies and a chorus from certain sectors of the construction industry that something "has to be done". Eventually, with joint funding from the Government and the industry, Sir Michael Latham was duly appointed to study construction procurement processes in the United Kingdom. He consulted widely within the construction industry while it was still in the middle of a recession.

Sir Michael Latham's report, *Constructing the team*,[3] was initially welcomed with broad support and acclamation. The Construction Industry Council set up numerous working groups to explore how many of Latham's recommendations could be made reality.

On closer inspection of Latham's report it became obvious that not everybody was prepared to accept that his recommendations should be implemented, whether by legislation or otherwise. The Government was being pressed continually to take some legislative initiative and the final result, after further consultation, was the Housing Grants, Construction and Regeneration Bill.

One of the difficulties facing the parliamentary draftsmen was to define a construction contract. There is no magic about construction contracts that makes them any different in principle from other contracts for sale of goods and supply of services. During the Bill's passage through Parliament the definition of a construction contract was debated at some length. The difference lies in identifying the subject matter or purpose of the contract. For this reason, the definition of a construction contract is the largest component of the provisions within Part II of the Act.

The Act deals with four main areas:

Part I: Grants for private sector housing
Part II: Construction contracts
Part III: Architects
Part IV: Grants for regeneration, development and relocation.

Part II (Construction Contracts) can be identified as comprising five sub-parts:

1. Definitions
2. Adjudication
3. Payments
4. Scheme for Construction Contracts
5. Miscellaneous

2 What is a construction contract?

Construction contracts

Part II of the Act starts with a broad definition of a construction contract. Exploration of this definition will require an understanding of sections 104 to 107 inclusive.

Section 104(1) provides:

> *"In this Part a "construction contract" means an agreement with a person for any of the following—*
>
> *(a) the carrying out of construction operations;*
>
> *(b) arranging for the carrying out of construction operations by others, whether under sub-contract to him or otherwise;*
>
> *(c) providing his own labour, or the labour of others, for the carrying out of construction operations."*

A person includes, by reference to the Interpretation Act 1978, corporations and limited companies as well as individuals. Person also includes the Crown, which is dealt with in detail in section 117.

An agreement for the carrying out of construction operations requires little explanation and will include main contracts and sub-contracts for the undertaking of works that fall within the definition of construction operations; see later at section 105. Less obviously many collateral warranties will fall within the scope of section 104(1)(a).

An agreement with a person under which one party arranges for the carrying out of construction operations will include management contracts. However, there is no guidance as to the full meaning of "arranging" unlike the definition of "arranges" in regulation 2(ii) of the Construction (Design and Management) Regulations 1994 (the CDM Regulations), see Appendix 4. Consideration of the scope of "arranging" as defined by the CDM Regulations may assist in understanding the full extent of "arranging" for interpreting section 104(1)(b).[4]

An agreement for a person to provide his or her own labour or the labour of others will include self-employed operatives and "labour only" sub-contractors.

Section 104(2) provides an extension of the definition of construction contract as follows:

> *"References in this Part to a construction contract include an agreement—*
>
> *(a) to do architectural, design, or surveying work, or*
>
> *(b) to provide advice on building, engineering, interior or exterior decoration or on the laying-out of landscape,*
>
> *in relation to construction operations."*

This section ensures that services provided by construction professionals will be within the scope of the Act, provided that such services are in relation to construction operations. Such services will include early design studies for feasibility purposes through to and including the completion of the construction operations. The services of construction professionals for post-contract services involving claims and dispute resolution are also included if it involves "surveying work". However, advising on the merits of a claim or acting for one of the parties in a forum for dispute resolution is likely to fall outside the scope of the categories of professional services identified in (2)(a) and (2)(b).

Section 104(3) provides:

> *"References in this Part to a construction contract do not include a contract of employment (within the meaning of the Employment Rights Act 1996)."*

This subsection ensures that the employer/employee relationship is not subject to the provisions of this Act.

Section 104(4) provides:

> *"The Secretary of State may by order add to, amend or repeal any of the provisions of subsection (1), (2) or (3) as to the agreements which are construction contracts for the purposes of this Part or are to be taken or not to be taken as included in references to such contracts.*
>
> *No such order shall be made unless a draft of it has been laid before and approved by a resolution of each of [sic] House of Parliament."*

This subsection leaves the Secretary of State with the opportunity to vary the scope and extent of construction contracts.

Before the Secretary of State could add to, amend or repeal any of the above subsections, the order effecting such change requires approval by resolution of the House of Commons and House of Lords.

Section 104(5) provides:

> *"Where an agreement relates to construction operations and other matters, this Part applies to it only so far as it relates to construction operations.*

An agreement relates to construction operations so far as it makes provision of any kind within subsection (1) or (2)."

While there can be no doubt that agreements where the primary purpose of the agreement relates to construction operations will be subject to the provisions of this Act, there are many other agreements where the construction operations are subsidiary. A commonplace example would be a development agreement that will contain important provisions for the future landlord and tenant relationship under a lease. Such an agreement is not exempt from the Act on the basis of any argument that the construction operations are not the primary purpose. On the contrary, any part of an agreement which relates to construction operations will be subject to the Act, without affecting the other provisions of the agreement. If the distinction between construction operations and non-construction operations and other matters can be differentiated, a contract should establish which parts of it are subject to the provisions of the Act and which are not. Alternatively there is no reason why the contract cannot be expressed so as to be subject in its entirety to the provisions of the Act in so far as adjudication, and payments, are relevant.

Section 104(6) provides:

"This Part applies only to construction contracts which—

(a) are entered into after the commencement of this Part, and

(b) relate to the carrying out of construction operations in England, Wales or Scotland."

Commencement of Part II of the Act will be linked to the approval of the Scheme for Construction Contracts. Deciding whether a contract has been entered into, for the purposes of ascertaining whether it is subject to the provisions of the Act, will require careful analysis. In the case of contracts which have been executed as deeds and delivered before the commencement there should be certainty. Simple contracts under hand, duly signed, should also avoid any arguments, provided that they have been dated. Where, as is all too often the case in the construction industry, the written evidence of the contract is to be found in various documents, the date when agreement was reached may be difficult to determine. Often, the act of starting work on site may be the only means of fixing the date of entering into a contract.

All contracts relating to the carrying out of construction operations in England and Wales or Scotland are subject to the provisions of the Act, even if the parties to the agreement are overseas and select a law other than the law of England and Wales or Scotland to govern the construction contract. This is confirmed by sections 148(1), (2) and 104(7), which provides:

> *"This Part applies whether or not the law of England and Wales or Scotland is otherwise the applicable law in relation to the contract."*

The provisions of the Act are extended to Northern Ireland by an Order in Council in accordance with section 149 which provides:

> *"An Order in Council under paragraph 1(1)(b) of Schedule 1 to the Northern Ireland Act 1974 (legislation for Northern Ireland in the interim period) which states that it is made only for purposes corresponding to those of Part II (construction contracts) or section 142 (home energy efficiency schemes)—*
>
> *(a)   shall not be subject to paragraph 1(4) and (5) of that Schedule (affirmative resolution of both Houses of Parliament), but*
>
> *(b)   shall be subject to annulment in pursuance of a resolution of either House of Parliament."*

The meaning of "construction operations"

Construction operations are defined by section 105(1), which provides:

"In this Part "construction operations" means, subject as follows, operations of any of the following descriptions—

(a) *construction, alteration, repair, maintenance, extension, demolition or dismantling of buildings, or structures forming, or to form, part of the land (whether permanent or not);*

(b) *construction, alteration, repair, maintenance, extension, demolition or dismantling of any works forming, or to form, part of the land, including (without prejudice to the foregoing) walls, roadworks, power-lines, telecommunication apparatus, aircraft runways, docks and harbours, railways, inland waterways, pipe-lines, reservoirs, water-mains, wells, sewers, industrial plant and installations for purposes of land drainage, coast protection or defence;*

(c) *installation in any building or structure of fittings forming part of the land, including (without prejudice to the foregoing) systems of heating, lighting, air-conditioning, ventilation, power supply, drainage, sanitation, water supply or fire protection, or security or communications systems;*

(d) *external or internal cleaning of buildings and structures, so far as carried out in the course of their construction, alteration, repair, extension or restoration;*

(e) *operations which form an integral part of, or are preparatory to, or are for rendering complete, such operations as are previously described in this subsection,*

including site clearance, earth-moving, excavation, tunnelling and boring, laying of foundations, erection, maintenance or dismantling of scaffolding, site restoration, landscaping and the provision of roadways and other access works;

(f)   painting or decorating the internal or external surfaces of any building or structure."

The definition of construction operations which is found in the Income and Corporation Taxes Act 1988 is related to buildings, structures and works. This is particularly noteworthy since there is no definition of any of these terms. Comparison with the definition of "construction work" as defined in regulation 2(i) of the CDM Regulations (see Appendix 3) reveals some striking differences. The CDM Regulations refer to the term "structure", which is widely defined, at regulation 2(i). Notable omissions from the definition of construction operations which are within the definition of construction work in the CDM Regulations include:

- fitting out, commissioning, renovation and upkeep.

- the installation, commissioning, maintenance, repair or removal of mechanical, electrical, gas, compressed air, hydraulic, telecommunications, computer or similar services which are normally fixed within or to a structure.

A detailed comparison of the definition of construction work and construction operations, in the CDM Regulations and the Act respectively, serves little purpose save to highlight that it cannot be assumed that because one construction project may fall within the scope of the CDM Regulations it will also fall within the scope of the Act (note in particular the activity of commissioning). For this reason, it is prudent to make an independent check, if there is any doubt, as to whether the construction work/operations fall within either or both definitions, or not at all.

Summary of key issues

Species of contracts subject to the provisions of the Act will include contracts for:

- supply of goods and services (including labour only) for construction operations
- development agreements and agreements for lease
- landlord and tenant works, respectively, under a lease
- project finance agreements
- appointment of professionals
- certain collateral warranties
- certain insurance policies.

The need to accommodate payment and adjudication provisions in accordance with the Act (if either or both are appropriate) to those parts of the above contracts which deal with construction operations.

Compare the definition of construction operations in the Act with the definition of construction work in the CDM Regulations since it is not necessarily the case that both will apply at the same time.

3 Exemptions from the Act

Specified construction operations

Despite a widely drafted definition of construction operations in section 105(1), section 105(2) sets out operations which are not within the definition of construction operations. Section 105(2) provides:

> *"The following operations are not construction operations within the meaning of this Part—*
>
> *(a) drilling for, or extraction of, oil or natural gas;*
>
> *(b) extraction (whether by underground or surface working) of minerals; tunnelling or boring, or construction of underground works, for this purpose;"*

Subsections (2)(a) and (b) describe operations which are connected with the mining, oil and gas industries.

> *"(c) assembly, installation or demolition of plant or machinery, or erection or demolition of steelwork for the purposes of supporting or providing access to plant or machinery, on a site where the primary activity is—*
>
> *(i) nuclear processing, power generation, or water or effluent treatment, or*
>
> *(ii) the production, transmission, processing or bulk storage (other than warehousing) of chemicals, pharmaceuticals, oil, gas, steel or food and drink;"*

The nature of the industries described in (c)(i) and (c)(ii) would appear to create the impression that a large tranche of operations, which would normally be considered as construction operations, are exempted from the Act. However, the extent of the operations which are exempt are limited to:

- assembly, installation or demolition of plant or machinery

- erection or demolition of steelwork for the purposes of supporting or providing access to plant or machinery.

The exemption of these construction operations is intended to recognise the

> "divergent views of the process industry and the building and civil engineering industries and their history as regards dispute resolution". (Viscount Ullswater, Hansard, Vol 570, No 70, col 1845)

In reality it may produce some very difficult distinctions. A contract which provides for the erection of primary and secondary steelwork, where the structural steelwork is in part used for "supporting or providing access to plant or machinery" will entail a mixture of construction operations, those which are, and those which are deemed not to be such. Without recognising this fact, a contract for the erection of steelwork may be subject to an adjudication procedure for some activities but not others. The practical approach will be to ensure that all such "mixed" construction contracts are subject in their entirety to the provisions of the Act.

> "(d) manufacture or delivery to site of—
>
> (i) building or engineering components or equipment,
>
> (ii) materials, plant or machinery, or
>
> (iii) components for systems of heating, lighting, air-conditioning, ventilation, power supply, drainage,

sanitation, water supply or fire protection, or for security or communications systems,

except under a contract which also provides for their installation;"

The exception for manufacture and delivery of the items in (i) to (iii) also extends to the professional services employed in designing the items described in section 104(2) because they would not be "in relation to construction operations". However, the exemption is lost by virtue of the exception when a manufacturer or supplier of any of the items in (i) to (iii) undertakes to fix or otherwise install the items, which would amount to construction operations. No doubt there will be arguments about the degree of fixity or installation for the purposes of deciding which side of the line a contract with a manufacturer or deliverer falls.

"(e) the making, installation and repair of artistic works, being sculptures, murals and other works which are wholly artistic in nature."

"Wholly artistic" suggests that any works or operations which have some functional benefit fall outside the scope of this definition.

Section 105(3) provides:

"The Secretary of State may by order add to, amend or repeal any of the provisions of subsection (1) or (2) as to the operations or work to be treated as construction operations for the purposes of this Part."

Section 105(4) provides:

"No such order shall be made unless a draft of it has been laid before and approved by a resolution of each House of Parliament."

Residential occupiers

Section 106(1) provides:

"This Part does not apply—

(a) to a construction contract with a residential occupier (see below), or

(b) to any other description of construction contract excluded from the operation of this Part by order of the Secretary of State."

A construction contract with a residential occupier is not subject to the provisions of Part II of the Act. The explanation of what characterises a construction contract with a residential occupier is set out in section 106(2) below.

At the time of writing there is no "other description of construction contract" excluded from the Act by an order of the Secretary of State, although the Secretary of State has kept the option open for some date in the future should changing circumstances make such an order desirable.

Section 106(2) provides:

"A construction contract with a residential occupier means a construction contract which principally relates to operations on a dwelling which one of the parties to the contract occupies, or intends to occupy, as his residence.

In this subsection "dwelling" means a dwelling-house or a flat; and for this purpose—

"dwelling-house" does not include a building containing a flat; and

"flat" means separate and self-contained premises constructed or adapted for use for residential purposes and forming part of a building from some other part of which the premises are divided horizontally."

The definition of "dwelling" is self-explanatory. However, the reference to "principally" to describe the main object of the construction contract suggests that a home office or other accommodation for commercial activity also comes within the scope of the exemption, provided that it is subsidiary to the principal purpose.

The exemption does not extend to other construction contracts which the party to a construction contract with a residential occupier might need to enter into for the purposes of performing the construction contract with a residential occupier. Therefore, the contract between a house builder, building a house for a residential occupier, and an architect is subject to the provisions of the Act.

Section 106(3) ensures that the exemption in respect of construction contracts with residential occupiers may be amended by the Secretary of State. It provides:

"The Secretary of State may by order amend subsection (2)."

The procedure which the Secretary of State has to adopt to obtain an order referred to in sections 106(1)(b) and 106(3) is set out at 106(4) which provides:

"No order under this section shall be made unless a draft of it has been laid before and approved by a resolution of each House of Parliament."

Unwritten agreements

Section 107(1) provides:

> *"The provisions of this Part apply only where the construction contract is in writing, and any other agreement between the parties as to any matter is effective for the purposes of this Part only if in writing.*
>
> *The expressions "agreement", "agree" and "agreed" shall be construed accordingly."*

This subsection is in two parts, firstly a reference to construction contracts, and secondly "any other agreement between the parties as to any matter".

A construction contract which is not in writing will not be subject to the Act's provisions despite the fact that all the elements required by common law of a contract are present. Thus, an unwritten construction contract is actionable but not subject to the Act and therefore the parties are denied the benefits and rights it provides.

The expression "any other agreement between the parties as to any matter" only makes sense if it is construed so that "any matter" relates to "construction operations". The second part of the subsection ensures that agreements which lack some of the common law characteristics of a contract, i.e. a quasi contract, a party to which would have to rely on a claim for *quantum meruit* will also be outside the scope of the Act if the agreement is unwritten.

Although the Act creates an exemption in the case of unwritten contracts the scope of what is acceptable as being in writing is widely construed; see the comments below on section 107(6). It is interesting to note that the remainder of section 107 is virtually identical to subsections 5(2) to 5(6) of the Arbitration Act 1996.

Section 107(2) provides:

> *"There is an agreement in writing—*

(a) *if the agreement is made in writing (whether or not it is signed by the parties),*

(b) *if the agreement is made by exchange of communications in writing, or*

(c) *if the agreement is evidenced in writing."*

Subsection (2)(a) is self-explanatory. However, proof will be required to establish that the written agreement is the agreement to which the parties have assented in circumstances where it has not been signed.

Many contracts come into existence by an exchange of correspondence and subsection (2)(b) provides that such an exchange is subject to the Act. The difficulties of proving which party's terms and conditions of contract apply arising from the familiar "battle of the forms" will be no different from other contracts which are not construction contracts.

Evidence in writing of a contract, dealt with by subsection (2)(c), leaves the door open for such evidence to come into existence after the commencement, or even completion, of the contract's performance. Thus, an invoice submitted by one party to the other may be sufficient evidence, as might a confirmation of verbal instructions set out in a letter. It is possible that the written evidence of an agreement could also be created by a third party who had sufficient knowledge, authority or proximity to the two contracting parties; see also the comments on section 107(4).

Section 107(3) provides:

"Where parties agree otherwise than in writing by reference to terms which are in writing, they make an agreement in writing."

By reference to section 107(6), the only other means of "otherwise than in writing" must be verbal, morse code, semaphore or other sign language! If during a non-written exchange between parties to a construction contract there is a reference to written terms and conditions of contract, in this context typically one of the standard forms of building or engineering contract, then the Act deems that such an agreement is an agreement in writing. The party contending for the argument that there was an agreement which referred to specific written terms and conditions would have to prove that there had been an unwritten reference to other written terms.

Section 107(4) provides:

"An agreement is evidenced in writing if an agreement made otherwise than in writing is recorded by one of the parties, or by a third party, with the authority of the parties to the agreement."

Thus, an agreement which is purely verbal but either recorded by "one of the parties" or "a third party, with the authority of the parties to the agreement" becomes an agreement in writing. Note that the subsection does not say "recorded in writing" since there is considerable overlap with subsection (2)(c).

Section 107(5) provides:

"An exchange of written submissions in adjudication pro-ceedings, or in arbitral or legal proceedings in which the existence of an agreement otherwise than in writing is alleged by one party against another party and not denied by the other party in his response constitutes as between those parties an agreement in writing to the effect alleged."

Even though written submissions, which include pleadings, are unlikely to come into existence until the construction operations are substantially or actually complete they may have the effect of creating *ex post facto* an agreement in writing. For written submissions or pleadings to have that effect the fact of an agreement otherwise than in writing must be contended for by one party and "not denied by the other party".

Section 107(6) provides:

> *"References in this Part to anything being written or in writing include its being recorded by any means."*

"Recorded by any means" will include handwriting, typing and storage on computer disks, but may also include an audio recording since this has not been specifically excluded. A tape recording of a telephone conversation is probably sufficient evidence to constitute an agreement in writing. Such audio recordings could be made by one party without the other's knowledge, although the burden of proof on the party who made the tape would be to prove that the recording was genuine and unedited.

Section 115(6) provides:

> *"References in this Part to a notice or other document include any form of communication in writing and references to service shall be construed accordingly."*

The need for notices or other documents to be in writing would appear to include audio tapes.

General comments

Recording any agreement in writing always has the benefit of introducing some certainty as to the terms and conditions which were agreed by the parties. The provisions of section 107 strain to admit any evidence of an agreement to the point where it is difficult to imagine many agreements for construction operations falling outside the scope of the Act. However, it is not uncommon for construction professionals to respond to verbal requests for services, nor is it uncommon for self-employed tradesmen to eschew paperwork. While the Act strains to have the widest possible definition of an agreement in writing, it must always be best advice to have a signed contract from the outset of any construction operations to avoid the difficulties of proof as to what the parties agreed when a dispute arises.

Summary of key issues

The need to identify and differentiate exempt construction operations from non-exempt construction operations under the same contract.

In respect of construction operations for a residential occupier, the need to consider the "principal" purpose of the works.

To note that the scope for a construction contract to be, or to remain, unwritten is extremely narrow.

4 Adjudication

Introduction to adjudication

One of the most significant recommendations made by Sir Michael Latham in *Constructing the team*[3] was the concept of a dispute resolution procedure to be applied at any stage during performance of a construction contract. Sir Michael Latham, and those who made representations to him, were not alone in seeking a form of dispute resolution which serves the needs of commercial organisations. The beginning of the 1990s has witnessed a growing disillusionment with litigation and arbitration and a commensurate interest in alternative dispute resolution, or ADR, the term by which it has now become widely known. Alongside this development, Lord Woolf conducted an enquiry into the administration of justice in the High Court and county courts which shall lead to the introduction of measures which, it is hoped, will provide cost-effective and more timely justice for all litigants.

ADR is a generic term which covers a number of dispute resolution procedures including mediation, conciliation, mini-trial and all their variants. Adjudication, as introduced by this Act, is a further example of ADR. Broadly, there are two categories of ADR. The first can be characterised by mediation or assisted negotiation. In other words, the parties still own their dispute and the means of its resolution. Conversely, the second category is where the parties, unable to resolve their dispute, hand over control of the decision making process to a third party. Adjudication is firmly within this second category because the adjudicator is required to make a "decision" which will bind the parties. This is discussed in more detail under section 108(2)(c).

There is an underlying and rarely addressed assumption that a speedy decision, good or bad, which lances the "boil" of a dispute is preferable because it serves the commercial needs of both parties more effectively. Justice is at best an elusive quality. The pursuit of justice relies traditionally on the collection, sifting and examination of all the evidence submitted by both parties to a dispute. The evidence is used to compare the contentions of each party with their strict legal rights. Unfortunately, in many instances it is not possible to be certain from the outset what those legal rights might be.

The procedures of litigation and arbitration represent the best attempts by parties within the jurisdiction of England and Wales to achieve justice. Procedures that rely on timetables with insufficient time to consider all the evidence and properly weigh the balance of legal rights will inevitably produce an outcome that is different in "quality" to the outcome of litigation or arbitration. There is, of course, no guarantee that one procedure will produce a "better" decision than the other. Indeed, any of the dispute resolution procedures have the potential to arrive at the same outcome. Despite the differences between adjudication and legal proceedings or arbitration, adjudication is a judicial process. Not only is a judicial process one which results in a decision binding on the parties, it should also not be contrary to the rules of natural justice, and should be non-arbitrary and referable back to the construction contract which sets out the agreement between the parties.

The Act has established some of the rules for adjudication and by doing so achieves a balance between the short-term advantages of adjudication without prejudicing the parties' right to have the dispute determined in later legal proceedings or arbitration.

Right to adjudication

Section 108(1) provides:

"A party to a construction contract has the right to refer a dispute arising under the contract for adjudication under a procedure complying with this section.

For this purpose "dispute" includes any difference."

Either party to a construction contract has the inalienable right to refer a dispute to adjudication. The right of a party to refer a dispute to an adjudicator cannot be objected to or denied by the other party. Any attempt within a construction contract to oust the right of either, or both, parties to refer a dispute to adjudication will be unenforceable.

The right only extends to a dispute which has arisen "under the contract", which is not as wide as "any dispute arising out of or under this contract" which could include tortious and contractual claims. The adjudication procedure must be one which complies with the remainder of section 108.

For the avoidance of doubt, the expression "dispute" is deemed to include any difference. This provision prevents the opportunity for a party to argue that there is no entitlement to refer any difference to adjudication.

Requirements

Section 108(2) sets out in paragraphs (a) to (f) the adjudication timetable, duty on the adjudicator and the basic procedure for adjudication arising under a construction contract.

Timetable

Section 108(2)(a) provides:

"The contract shall—

(a) enable a party to give notice at any time of his intention to refer a dispute to adjudication;"

Where a dispute exists between the parties, either party can give notice at any time of an intention to refer a dispute to adjudication. Thus, a notice can be given during the course of the construction operations or at any time thereafter.

The party who has decided to refer a dispute to adjudication ("the claimant") could have prepared or considered its basis of claim against the other party ("the respondent") in considerable detail before referring a dispute to adjudication. This will have a significant effect on the dynamics of adjudication and the administration of a construction contract as discussed later.

The terminology of the Act requires the claimant to "give notice" although section 115 refers to "service of any notice". The giving of a notice is used consistently in the other relevant sections and therefore "give notice" should be construed as "serve notice".

A notice should include:

- a reference to identify the construction contract, or part of the contract, which comes within the provisions of the Act

- the substance of the dispute, including where and when it has arisen

- the nature of the claim or relief which the claimant seeks.

A specimen form at Appendix 1 may be used as a precedent for the notice required by section 108(2)(a).

The claimant is required to serve the notice on the respondent in accordance with the provisions of section 115. If an adjudicator has been appointed, or an appointing body has been specified, the adjudicator or the appointing body should also receive a copy of

the notice at the same time as the notice is served on the respondent
to avoid wasting time.

Section 108(2)(b) provides:

> *"[The contract shall—]*
>
> *(b) provide a timetable with the object of securing the appointment of the adjudicator and referral of the dispute to him within 7 days of such notice;"*

To comply with this provision it is crucial that the timetable for
securing an appointment is agreed, otherwise the Scheme for
Construction Contracts will apply.

The Act does not provide a detailed timetable, merely a requirement that the adjudicator should be appointed within seven days
of such notice. The seven-day period will start from the first day
after the respondent has received the notice; see comments on
section 116.

The Act requires the timetable to be agreed as part of the
construction contract. The timetable is to have the "object" of
securing the appointment of an adjudicator and referral of the
dispute within seven days. The timetable, once the adjudicator has
been appointed, subject to paragraphs (c) and (d) of section 108(2),
will either become a matter for the adjudicator's directions or the
previously agreed rules of adjudication.

In the ideal situation, the construction contract will name an
adjudicator from the outset of the construction operations, or a list
of suitable persons from which the adjudicator will be selected. If
the first named person was unable or unwilling to act as the
adjudicator the next named person in the list would be asked to
act, and so on. Such an arrangement would ensure that there is the
best possible chance of securing the appointment of an adjudicator
before the seven days have elapsed. To have a named person, or
list of named persons, prepared to act as the adjudicator in a

construction contract would infer that the parties have agreed beforehand the suitability of those persons and the terms and conditions of the appointment.

The parties to a construction contract may agree to send the notice of intention to refer a dispute to adjudication to a specified appointing body. In this case, the appointing body would be responsible for forwarding the notice to an adjudicator to ensure an appointment was made within seven days. Without such an agreement as to the identity of the adjudicator, or list of adjudicators or an appointing body, prior to commencement of construction operations it is still possible for the parties to reach an agreement subsequently. The claimant should consider proposing the name of the adjudicator in the notice, for agreement by the respondent, although at this stage, in the absence of any agreement, the Scheme for Construction Contracts will apply.

The Scheme for Construction Contracts will provide the missing elements in any agreement, although it will be good practice to have agreed a set of rules for adjudication before an adjudicator has been appointed. The adjudication rules of the Official Referees Solicitors Association at Appendix 5, which comply with the provisions of section 108, can be used without amendment, or as the basis for further negotiations or development.

While the Act refers to the adjudicator as "him", by virtue of the Interpretation Act 1978 "him" is to be construed as including "her".

Section 108(2)(c) provides:

> *"[The contract shall—]*
>
> *(c) require the adjudicator to reach a decision within 28 days of referral or such longer period as is agreed by the parties after the dispute has been referred;"*

Because an adjudicator's appointment cannot be bound by the terms and conditions of the construction contract, this section requires that the parties agree that the terms and conditions of the adjudicator's joint appointment (either in the agreed rules for adjudication or in the Scheme for Construction Contracts) shall require *inter alia* the adjudicator to reach a decision within 28 days of referral or such longer period in accordance with section 108(2). The adjudicator should be made aware that the requirement to reach a decision within 28 days, or longer as provided for by the Act, is a statutory duty.

What the Act omits to specify is the nature of the decision which the adjudicator is required to reach. It does not require specifically that the decision should be one which completely disposes of the dispute between the parties. An adjudicator's decision may only be an interim or preliminary decision; conversely the adjudicator is at liberty to make a decision that the dispute should be decided with another adjudication.

The Act does not state expressly when the decision should be communicated by the adjudicator to the parties, nor how the decision should be communicated, whether in writing with reasons or otherwise. These are all matters to be agreed between the parties in the rules for adjudication and/or in the terms and conditions of the adjudicator's joint appointment. In the absence of any of these matters having been agreed, the Scheme for Construction Contracts, discussed in Chapter 6, may clarify the nature of the adjudicator's decision.

The period of 28 days is counted from the date after the day when the respondent has referred the dispute to adjudication. In counting a period of 28 days a few days can be a major issue if it is unclear when precisely the dispute was "referred". Is it when the adjudicator accepts the appointment or from when the claimant submits a full written claim?

There is no scope in the Act to have the period of 28 days extended unless:

- *both* parties agree to an extension of time after the dispute has been referred, or

- an extension is allowed by virtue of paragraph (d); see below.

Section 108(2)(d) provides:

> *"[The contract shall—]*
>
> *(d) allow the adjudicator to extend the period of 28 days by up to 14 days, with the consent of the party by whom the dispute was referred;"*

The adjudicator is allowed to extend the time in which the adjudicator is required to reach a decision by up to 14 days, but only if the claimant consents to such an extension. This opportunity for the claimant to withhold consent (there being no requirement as to reasonableness) can place a particularly onerous burden on the adjudicator and the respondent.

There is no statutory penalty on the adjudicator for failing to reach a decision within the time limits. However, if the adjudicator fails to reach a decision within the time limits set out in the Act, it is unclear what remedy either or both parties would have against the adjudicator. It is extremely doubtful if there is any, unless the adjudicator is in breach of the adjudicator's terms and conditions of appointment, by virtue of section 108(4), unless such a breach is in bad faith.

Duty on the adjudicator

While there is no guidance in section 108 to the parties to assist them in determining what qualifications and experience are appropriate for a person to act as an adjudicator, there is an express direction in section 108(2)(e) which provides:

> *"[The contract shall—]*

(e) impose a duty on the adjudicator to act impartially; and"

Such a duty is not surprising; indeed, the Arbitration Act 1996 imposes the same duty on an arbitrator. The Act requires the construction contract to impose the duty of impartiality on the adjudicator, which should therefore be expressly set out in the adjudicator's terms and conditions of appointment or adjudication rules.

What is significant is not what section 108(2)(e) requires, but what it does not require. There is no requirement that an adjudicator should be independent. This lack of need to be independent raises the prospect of adjudicators being appointed who, in some way, are connected with either of the parties or a third party involved in the construction operations. At one extreme, the connection might be an employer/employee relationship with one of the parties or, at the other, a consultant who has been instructed by one of the parties on some previous projects.

An adjudicator would be well advised to declare any connection with either or both of the parties before accepting an appointment.

Breach by an adjudicator of the duty to act impartially would provide an opportunity for one of the parties to challenge the adjudicator's decision in the courts under section 108(4), see below, or simply to ignore the decision and await the actions by the other party to seek enforcement of the decision.

Procedure to be adopted for adjudication

Section 108(2)(f) provides:

"[The contract shall—]

(f) enable the adjudicator to take the initiative in ascertaining the facts and the law."

The person appointed as adjudicator should not therefore be constrained by the previous agreement of the parties with regard to any procedure to ascertain facts and law. The initiative granted to the adjudicator should enable the adjudication procedure to be tailored to all the circumstances of the dispute to be adjudicated. The matters which an adjudicator is at liberty to decide include, among other matters:

- whether to adopt an adversarial or inquisitorial approach

- whether the mode of presentation of the claimant's case and the respondent's response should be wholly written or verbal, or a combination of both

- the venue for the adjudication

- the need or otherwise for site visits

- the need and procedure for inspection of documents

- which rules (if any) of evidence are applicable

- the extent and presentation of expert evidence (if any).

For a more complete list see rule 19 of the ORSA Adjudication Rules at Appendix 5.

Whatever approach the adjudicator chooses to adopt in ascertaining the facts and the law, the adjudicator's conduct should be impartial and in good faith; see section 108(4) below.

Since adjudication is a judicial process, the objective of which is to ascertain the facts and the law, an adjudicator should ideally be a person who has:

- a knowledge of the technical and commercial issues connected with the dispute, and

- a thorough understanding of the law, which will enable the adjudicator to recognise, analyse and decide upon all legal issues arising under the contract which concern the dispute.

Various organisations have established an accreditation system for persons who wish to hold themselves out as available or willing to accept appointments as adjudicators and may even act as appointing bodies. However, the parties to a construction contract are entirely free to choose whoever they can agree upon (unless the contract provides otherwise) to act as the adjudicator, subject to the application of the Scheme for Construction Contracts.

Decision of the adjudicator

Section 108(3) provides:

> *"The contract shall provide that the decision of the adjudicator is binding until the dispute is finally determined by legal proceedings, by arbitration (if the contract provides for arbitration or the parties otherwise agree to arbitration) or by agreement.*
>
> *The parties may agree to accept the decision of the adjudicator as finally determining the dispute."*

Whatever decision the adjudicator reaches within the statutory timetable, or otherwise extended by agreement, it is binding on the parties until there is a subsequent and contrary decision in legal proceedings or arbitration. The Court of Appeal has referred to decisions of adjudicators as having an "ephemeral and subordinate character".[5] While the content and nature of the adjudicator's decision has been discussed above under section 108(2)(c), there remains some doubt as to whether a court will enforce a decision of the adjudicator in all cases depending on the machinery of the contract. The decision of the adjudicator in *A. Cameron Limited* v *John Mowlem & Company plc* was expressed to be binding in the form of sub-contract. Nonetheless the Court of Appeal declined to enforce the adjudicator's decision on two grounds. Firstly, that the application under the Arbitration Act 1952 was misconceived as it was not an arbitration award, and secondly that the adjudicator was not empowered to determine all disputes under the contract. By contrast, any future applications to enforce an adjudicator's decision would rely on this section within the Act and, moreover, section 108 does not limit the nature of the dispute to be determined by adjudication provided that it arises under the contract. Any failure of a court to enforce a decision of an adjudicator would be disappointing since it would be at odds with the spirit of the legislation. However, the parties can agree that a decision of the adjudicator is binding to the extent that the parties shall be entitled to summary enforcement, as provided for in the ORSA Adjudication Rules.

A party who is dissatisfied with the adjudicator's decision has no right of appeal against the decision on the basis that it is wrong in law or fact. The only exception is in the case of a challenge to an adjudicator's decision on the basis that the adjudicator was guilty of misconduct. That is to say, that the adjudicator was in breach of the duty to act impartially and, or alternatively, acted in bad faith. Such a challenge may not be worthwhile. Either party can still have the dispute resolved by legal proceedings or arbitration if there is dissatisfaction with the decision of the adjudicator. Indeed, it is open to either party, unless the construction contract provides otherwise, to issue legal proceedings or refer the dispute to arbitration at the same time as the dispute is referred to adjudication.

There is no provision in the Act to suggest that the decision of the adjudicator should not be disclosed to a judge or arbitrator whether those proceedings are concurrent or subsequent to the adjudication procedure. However, disclosure of all the "evidence" and the adjudicator's decision, whether or not it was given with reasons, could be prejudicial to the party against whom the decision was given. For this reason, the parties should consider agreeing that the adjudication procedure is without prejudice and confidential.

Liability of the adjudicator

Section 108(4) provides:

> *"The contract shall also provide that the adjudicator is not liable for anything done or omitted in the discharge or purported discharge of his functions as adjudicator unless the act or omission is in bad faith, and that any employee or agent of the adjudicator is similarly protected from liability."*

It is because of this section, if for no other reason, that the appointment of the adjudicator should be given very serious consideration. The adjudicator can make any number of errors in deciding matters of fact and law without fear of any action by either of the parties for the recovery of damages save in respect of any decision determined by bad faith. Breach of the duty to act impartially would generally amount to an act or omission in bad faith.

This section refers to employees or agents of the adjudicator as also benefiting from the immunity from liability. One of the characteristics of legal proceedings and arbitration is that the person acting as judge or arbitrator is an individual. This is to be contrasted with the quasi-arbitral role of the architect or engineer under certain standard forms of building contract where it has become commonplace to name limited companies or partnerships. The reference to "any employee or agent" suggests that the adjudicator may also be a limited company or partnership, although it is doubtful whether this is likely to be acceptable in practice. In other circumstances the provision extends immunity from liability to any appointing body which takes responsibility for appointing adjudicators.

Section 108(5) provides:

> *"If the contract does not comply with the requirements of subsections (1) to (4), the adjudication provisions of the Scheme for Construction Contracts apply."*

An indication of what the Scheme for Construction Contracts will include is given by section 108(6), which provides:

"For England and Wales, the Scheme may apply the provisions of the Arbitration Act 1996 with such adaptations and modifications as appear to the Minister making the scheme to be appropriate.

For Scotland, the Scheme may include provision conferring powers on courts in relation to adjudication and provision relating to the enforcement of the adjudicator's decision."

The consultation paper issued by the Department of the Environment entitled *Making the Scheme for Construction Contracts* provides a further indication of what might be included in the Scheme for Construction Contracts.[6] The consultation paper helpfully identifies a number of key issues for consideration in drafting any set of adjudication rules, which have been used at the end of this chapter under the summary of key issues.

Commercial consequences

The speed of the adjudication process and the binding nature of the adjudicator's decision may be very appealing to the parties to a construction contract. This appeal may lead to frequent referrals as a party to a construction contract can refer any dispute to adjudication at any time. There is the prospect therefore of numerous concurrent and/or separate adjudications under the same construction contract, although the parties may agree that different adjudication proceedings can be consolidated. Moreover, not all adjudication decisions will have necessarily been given by the same adjudicator for a whole host of reasons. Only the simplest of construction projects will be the subject of one construction contract; therefore on complex projects involving construction operations where there are numerous construction contracts, the number of adjudications arising from construction projects could be legion. The only effective brake on parties constantly referring disputes to adjudication will be the cost and manpower which will be absorbed by the adjudication process.

Used tactically, the adjudication procedure is a powerful tool to resolve differences, not least because it favours the claimant who can take advantage of thorough preparation before referring a dispute to adjudication. The worst of all scenarios is the creation of a new construction claims industry and profession of adjudicators. Certainly, there will be new skills required for preparing a claim and defence in adjudication and new skills will be required of the adjudicator to manage the procedure to its conclusion. Time will tell whether the benefits claimed for adjudication by Sir Michael Latham and its other protagonists are proven. In the meantime, parties to a construction contract should not forget that there are other forms of dispute resolution, alternative or otherwise, which are not ousted by the Act.

Summary of key issues

In drafting the rules of adjudication annexed to a construction contract or the terms and conditions of the adjudicator's appointment, the following issues, based on those identified in the consultation paper *Making the Scheme for Construction Contracts* published by the Department of the Environment in November 1996, should be considered:

1. Primary and associated issues which have to be included in a construction contract to comply with the Act:

Section 108(2)(a)
What should be the arrangements for modification?
- Any time
- Notice in writing
- Served in accordance with section 115
- Identification of the parties to be served with the notice

Section 108(2)(b)
How may the adjudicator be selected?
- After consideration of the qualifications of the adjudicator(s)
- Agree list at the outset of a construction contract, or
- Agree appointing body
- By subsequent agreement

How should the appointment be made and confirmed?
What should constitute referral?

Section 108(2)(c)&(d)
What overall time limits apply?
- The adjudicator must reach his or her decision within 28 days
- The parties may agree, after the dispute has been referred, to approve extensions of any length

- An extension, or extensions, not exceeding 14 days in total may be approved by the claimant

Section 108(2)(e)
How to impose a duty on the adjudicator to act impartially?
- Express term in the adjudication rules and/or appointment

Section 108(2)(f)
What powers should be given to the adjudicator to ascertain the facts and the law?
- Require the delivery of written statements of case by a fixed date
- Production of documents by a fixed date
- Limit the length of any written or oral submissions
- Require the attendance of any party, or employee or agent of any party, for questioning at any reasonable time, with or without presence of other parties
- Make site visits
- Reliance on own specialist knowledge
- Obtain advice from specialist consultants
- Make directions for conduct of the adjudication
- Conduct the adjudication inquisitorially or adversarially
- Review and revision of previous directions and issue such other directions as he or she considers to be appropriate

Section 108(3)
How shall the contract provide that the decision of the adjudicator is binding?
- An express entitlement to summary judgement for enforcement of the decision
- Preserve the right of either party to have the dispute determined by legal proceedings or arbitration
- The parties may, at any time, agree the decision of the adjudicator has finally determined the dispute

Section 108(4)
How to preserve the adjudicator's (and any other employee's or agent's) immunity from liability?

- Express term in the adjudication rules and/or appointment excluding liability except for acts or omissions in bad faith

2. Supplementary considerations for drafting adjudication rules, which are not mandatory:

- Who should be able to serve as an adjudicator?
- Should information be provided to a potential adjudicator, and if so what information?
- Matters of privacy, confidentiality and subsequent use of information and decision of the adjudicator in subsequent proceedings
- May the adjudicator make more than one decision?
- What scope should there be for consolidation with other proceedings?
- Should the adjudicator's decision include reasons?
- Should the decision be in writing?
- Can decisions be subject to correction by the adjudicator?
- How should payments ordered by the adjudicator be treated?
- Who should be liable for the adjudicator's fees and expenses?
- Should the adjudicator have any power with regard to parties' costs?
- What should happen if an agreed adjudicator is unable or unwilling to act either before or during the adjudication procedure?
- In what circumstances should it be possible to remove an adjudicator?
- What should happen if the adjudicator fails to make a decision within the time limits, or any decision at all?
- Can a party pursue concurrent proceedings in litigation or arbitration?

5 Payments

Entitlement to stage payments

Section 109(1) provides:

> "A party to a construction contract is entitled to payment by instalments, stage payments or other periodic payments for any work under the contract unless—
>
> (a) it is specified in the contract that the duration of the work is to be less than 45 days, or
>
> (b) it is agreed between the parties that the duration of the work is estimated to be less than 45 days."

Payments may either be instalments, stage payments or periodic payments. None of these terms are defined, although they all have a subtly different meaning by reference to any good dictionary.

An instalment is one of a series of partial payments. For example, payment by instalments for hire purchase of goods often denotes payment of an amount which is equal to all the other payments, save the first and/or the final payment. A stage payment suggests one which may be paid when a predetermined point is reached in the works, or a defined section of the works is completed. Finally, a periodic payment suggests payments made at a date which falls on the anniversary of all the previous payments although the amount of the payment does not necessarily have to be the same in every case.

Thus, subject to the duration of the works being 45 days or longer, there is an entitlement enjoyed by one party to payment, the payee, before the final payment, subject to all other contract conditions having been satisfied. Payments do not have to be the same amount or made at equal intervals in time.

Section 109(1)(a) applies where the construction contract specifies that the contractual time limit for undertaking and completing the works is 45 days or less. Alternatively, section 109(1)(b) applies where the parties may agree that their mutual estimate of the duration of the work is 45 days or less, in circumstances where there is no specified contractual time limit. Consider the situation where a contractor submits a pre-contract programme for the intended work which indicates the time required to complete the work is 44 days or less. In circumstances where there was no specified contractual time limit, and perhaps even if there was, and the programme was accepted by the other party, the statutory entitlement to some payment, or payments, before the final payment would be lost.

Section 109(2) provides:

"The parties are free to agree the amounts of the payments and the intervals at which, or circumstances in which, they become due."

At the pre-contract stage, the parties should have agreed:

- the basis for determining the amount of the payments
- the date or other circumstances when the payments become due.

These details are required to be set out in the construction contract by virtue of section 110(1); see below.

What section 109(1) appears to give by way of a right to interim payments can be altered by virtue of section 109(2). If a party resists making an unfavourable agreement under which the benefit of an interim payment would be lost, the Scheme for Construction Contracts will imply the appropriate terms in the absence of an agreement by virtue of section 109(3), which provides:

"In the absence of such agreement, the relevant provisions of the Scheme for Construction Contracts apply."

The following sections, 110 to 113 inclusive, refer and relate to payments, and section 109(4) provides:

"References in the following sections to a payment under the contract include a payment by virtue of this section."

Dates for payment

Section 110(1) provides:

"Every construction contract shall—

(a) provide an adequate mechanism for determining what payments become due under the contract, and when, and

(b) provide for a final date for payment in relation to any sum which becomes due.

The parties are free to agree how long the period is to be between the date on which a sum becomes due and the final date for payment."

One of the difficulties with this section is the lack of a definition, or any guidance, as to what constitutes "an adequate mechanism" for determining what payments become due, and when, under a construction contract. Since the parties are free to fix the period of time between the date on which a payment is due and the final date for payment, it must be implicit that the parties are also free to agree the "adequate mechanism".

The amount of the payment is a valuation matter. There are numerous variations available to the parties to determine what amount is due. The basic means of valuation will include one, or a combination, of the following:

- agreed schedule of pre-determined payments

- measure and value in accordance with bills of quantities and/or schedules of rates

- reimbursement of costs generally or for identified items

- time-related costs.

Save in respect of the agreed schedule of pre-determined payments, one party's view can be, and often is, very different from the other party's as to the value of the works. The standard forms of contract in common usage in the construction industry, between the employer and the main contractor, recognise the need for the main contractor to have an input into valuing the works; but, simply because the contractor values the works in accordance with the agreed mechanism for valuation, it does not necessarily mean that the employer agrees that the work has been completed, or has been completed satisfactorily. Therefore, the assessment by the employer of the contractor's valuation will often be an important part of the adequate mechanism. The evidence of the employer's assessment of the amount due is dealt with in subsection (2); see below. The reference to employer and contractor is merely for ease of explanation because the need to provide an adequate mechanism for determining what payments are due applies to all contractual relationships on a project, i.e. payer and payee.

Until the provisions of Part II of this Act were introduced, the mechanism as to whether payments became due was, and continues to be, often fixed by reference to one of the following:

- a schedule of agreed dates

- an agreed period of time after the payee has submitted an application for payment

- an agreed period of time from a certificate issued by, or on behalf of, the payer.

The parties are free to agree the length of the period between the date on which a sum becomes due and the final date for payment. The parties are also free to agree when the payments become due under the contract. Thus, the parties are free to agree that the date on which a sum becomes due, in respect of work completed in month one, is the first day of month three or four, or any other date, unless it cannot be fixed or determined in advance within the adequate mechanism.

Since the final date for payment is not necessarily the date on which payment is due (and is quite unlikely to be so when read in conjunction with section 110(2)), the parties can select any mutually agreeable period between these two dates. The result may lead to unnecessarily protracted mechanisms for determining the amount of payment and the date on which it is due. At the least, the provisions of this section should avoid arbitrarily timed payments or open-ended commitments to make actual payment.

The unequal bargaining power between many contracting parties in construction projects may result in very extended periods of time between the final date for payment and completion of the work in respect of the payment. This may take on increasing significance, particularly between contractors and their subcontractors, with the prohibition of conditional payment provisions (i.e. pay when paid clauses) under section 113; see below. Section 110(2) provides:

"Every construction contract shall provide for the giving of notice by a party not later than five days after the date on which a payment becomes due from him under the contract, or would have become due if—

(a) *the other party had carried out his obligations under the contract, and*

(b) *no set-off or abatement was permitted by reference to any sum claimed to be due under one or more other contracts,*

specifying the amount (if any) of the payment made or proposed to be made, and the basis on which that amount was calculated."

The party from which a payment becomes due under this section (the payer) is under an obligation to give a notice to the other party (the payee) specifying the amount, if any, of a payment made or proposed to be made. The notice must be given even if, for other reasons, there are no payments due to be made by the payer.

The timing of the notice is fixed solely by reference to a latest date. The notice must be given not later than five days after the agreed date, by reference to subsection (1) above, when the payment is due under the contract. In many situations, the notice is likely to be given earlier than the date on which payment is due, if such a date has allowed sufficient time for the payer to ascertain the amount due from the date when the works, in respect of which payment is due, have been completed. Conversely, the notice can be given after payment has been made.

The contents of the notice must specify clearly the amount of the payment, if any, or by inference, the amount due from the payee in respect of any prior overpayment. However, the specified amount cannot be arbitrary. The basis on which the amount was calculated must be set out in the notice, although the section does not expressly require calculations, detailed or otherwise. If the mechanism for determining the amount due has been agreed between the parties, this should enable the payee to verify the amount due independently. If the payee disagrees with the amount due given in the notice, that is the basis of a dispute which can be referred to adjudication.

The basis on which the amount was calculated must assume that the payee has carried out its obligations under the contract. The obligations include compliance with relevant specifications for workmanship and materials. This suggests that full credit should be given in respect of completed work for which the payee claims, even if the completed work is defective and not worth the full amount claimed by the payee. For example, the payee seeks payment for a pump which has not reached an output performance specification. The payer should value the work in accordance with the contract as though the pump had achieved the specified output performance, but should then identify the deduction made from the full amount in a section 111 notice.

The amount specified in the notice given by the payer cannot take into account any sums which the payer contends are sums representing a set-off, or abatement, under other contracts between the two parties, or otherwise (see Appendix 6 for a brief explanation of set-off and abatement). Thus, although the right to set-off or abate sums arising under other unconnected contracts may exist (either because there is an express power given to the payer in the contract, or there are special circumstances sufficiently connecting one claim under another contract with the contract under which the notice is given), these may not be taken into account when specifying the amount due. This should be contrasted with the situation involving defective work in the previous paragraph.

To summarise, it is possible to discern as many as five stages associated with the "adequate mechanism". These are:

Stage 1:   the payee prepares and submits to the payer an application for payment

Stage 2: the payer reviews and assesses the amount payable to the payee

Stage 3: the payer gives a notice to the payee, in accordance with section 110(2) specifying the amount (if any) due to the payee, either before a date when payment becomes due under the contract, or within five days thereafter

Stage 4: the payer gives a notice of intention to withhold payment to the payee, in accordance with section 111, see below

Stage 5: the payer makes payment of the amount due on, or before, the final date for payment.

Note that stages 2, 3 and 4 can be dealt with together as one stage, or two stages, instead of three separate stages.

Section 110(3) provides:

> *"If or to the extent that a contract does not contain such provision as is mentioned in subsection (1) or (2), the relevant provisions of the Scheme for Construction Contracts apply."*

The relevant provisions of the Scheme for Construction Contracts have yet to be approved by both Houses of Parliament but a construction contract which does not have provision for:

- an adequate mechanism for determining what payments are due, and when

- the final date for payment in relation to any sum which becomes due

- the timing of the notice required by section 110(2)

will have the relevant terms implied by the Scheme for Construction Contracts.

Therefore, many claims made by contractors for payment on a *quantum meruit* will, in fact, be determined by the Scheme for

Construction Contracts, or at least that is the hope, in circumstances where:

- all that exists is an express agreement to pay a reasonable sum in respect of work done, or

- work has been completed under a contract where there was no mechanism for determining the amount due.

The other situations in which a contractor is entitled to claim on a *quantum meruit* may or may not come within the terms of the Act. These are a quasi-contract. This situation occurs where a contractor carries out work while the essential terms of the contract are still being negotiated. If a contractor carries out work or renders services under a contract that is subsequently found to be void, it would depend on the grounds on which the contract was void whether the provisions of the Act would avoid the need to bring a claim on a *quantum meruit*. In certain circumstances a contractor carrying out work outside of an agreed contract may, or may not, depending on the facts, be able to claim a *quantum meruit* or rely on the provisions of the Act.

Notice of intention to withhold payment

Section 111(1) provides:

> "*A party to a construction contract may not withhold payment after the final date for payment of a sum due under the contract unless he has given an effective notice of intention to withhold payment.*"

On or before the final date for payment, established in accordance with section 110, the payer should have made a payment of the sum referred to in section 110(2), subject to the further provisions of this section. Although it is not expressly stated, it is implicit that the payer cannot withhold all, or part, of the sum due under the contract in the section 110(2) notice without having given an effective notice to the other of an intention to do so. Therefore, if the payer has any objection to making a full payment for any reason, this section imposes a strict requirement on the need to serve an effective notice. The section 111 notice has separate requirements as compared with the notice under section 110(2), although the remainder of section 111(1) permits the notice of intention to withhold payment to be merged with the section 110(2) notice. It provides:

> *"The notice mentioned in section 110(2) may suffice as a notice of intention to withhold payment if it complies with the requirements of this section."*

To comply with the requirements of section 111, the notice has to be an effective notice. Section 111(2) sets out the specific requirements of a notice to ensure it is effective. Section 111(2) provides:

> *"To be effective such a notice must specify—*
>
> *(a) the amount proposed to be withheld and the ground for withholding payment, or*
>
> *(b) if there is more than one ground, each ground and the amount attributable to it,*
>
> *and must be given not later than the prescribed period before the final date for payment."*

The first requirement is the specification of the amount proposed to be withheld. "Specify" does not necessarily imply a requirement to show the calculations or rationale for determining the amount proposed to be withheld. The lack of an express requirement to prepare an ascertainable amount appears to leave open the prospect of inflated estimates of the cost associated with each ground for withholding payments.

The ground for withholding payment must be specified in the notice, which may include:

- workmanship and/or materials not in accordance with the specification

- liquidated damages for delay

- previous overpayment

- damage to property

- disruption to the work of others.

While there is no doubt that these examples may provide grounds for withholding payment under the contract, the possibility of withholding money by reason of a set-off or abatement under one or more other contracts has not been excluded expressly. The inability to deduct sums from the section 110(2) notice by reference to one or more other contracts is not repeated for the purposes of the section 111 notice. Therefore, provided that a contract permits the withholding of payment, in part or otherwise, by reference to another contract, or contracts, this may be another ground to withhold payment. Even if there are no cross-contractual rights to withhold payment, the section does not exclude the possibility of an equitable set-off where the circumstances are sufficiently connected, that to oust the right to withhold payment under the contract would be inequitable.

The notice must set out each and every ground on which the payer relies to justify the withholding of the payment and the amount attributable to each ground.

The notice must be given not later than the prescribed period before the final date for payment. Thus, a notice of intention to withhold payment given on or after the final date for payment, or after the prescribed period, will be ineffective and the entitlement to withhold payment from the sum due under the contract on that occasion will be lost. There is no express provision in section 111 to prevent the amount in one ineffective notice being carried over to a subsequent notice. Section 111(3) deals with the question as to what the prescribed period should be and provides:

> *"The parties are free to agree what the prescribed period is to be.*
>
> *In the absence of such agreement, the period shall be that provided by the Scheme for Construction Contracts."*

Where the parties do not enjoy equal bargaining strength the "prescribed period" could, in the extreme, be as little as only one day before the final date for payment. If short prescribed periods are agreed, it provides the payer with the maximum opportunity to investigate and evaluate the grounds for withholding payment and puts the payee at a disadvantage in challenging the notice before the lesser amount is paid.

If the construction contract omits any reference to the prescribed period the Scheme for Construction Contracts shall provide a prescribed period.

Section 111(4) provides:

> *"Where an effective notice of intention to withhold payment is given, but on the matter being referred to adjudication it is decided that the whole or part of the amount should be paid, the decision shall be construed as requiring payment not later than—*
>
> *(a)   seven days from the date of the decision, or*
>
> *(b)   the date which apart from the notice would have been the final date for payment,*
>
> *whichever is the later."*

The payee who receives an effective notice and who disagrees with the amount being withheld, either because one or some of the grounds or the amount attributed to any ground is disputed, has a two stage strategy. Firstly, to negotiate within the framework of the construction contract to seek a review of the notice, and secondly, if that fails, to refer the dispute to adjudication.

If the prescribed period is generous, the opportunity for negotiation (and possibly adjudication) may bring about a revision to the amount intended to be withheld stated in the notice, otherwise the payee is in the position of pursuing a remedy after the payment has been withheld.

If the payee contends that the notice is ineffective, pressure can be applied by the payee exercising its rights under section 112 to suspend performance of the contract (see below), although this would be a high-risk strategy if there were an arguable case that the notice was effective.

In referring the matter to adjudication, the payee has the comfort of knowing that the adjudicator's decision will be made not later than 28 days after the referral of the dispute, unless the payee agrees to an extension of time for the giving of the decision. If the adjudicator decides that the whole, or any part, of the amount which the payer seeks to withhold should be paid, the payer is required to make payment within seven days of the decision, in circumstances where the final date for payment under section 110(1)(b) has been passed. Therefore, where the final date for payment has not passed, the payer should make payment on the final date for payment, although if this is less than seven days after the adjudicator's decision, or later than the final date for payment, the payer will have a period of seven days in which to make arrangements for the payment.

Although the resolution of a dispute over payment is a quick procedure, it is likely that the next payment after the disputed payment will have been paid, or should have been paid, before the adjudicator's decision. Since the problem which had caused the original dispute will not have been resolved in time for the subsequent payments there is the likelihood that these payments will also be disputed. The potential thus exists for an unscrupulous payer to abuse the system and create an adjudication nightmare.

Right to suspend performance for non-payment

A party who is in the process of providing goods and services to another party under a construction contract has always had a common-law right to stop further work if the other party repudiates the contract. A failure to make a payment, under certain circumstances where there is a contractual duty to make such a payment, can amount to repudiation. Accepting the defaulting party's repudiation would usually entail stopping the work.

Some construction contracts, prior to the introduction of Part II of the Act, may have provided an express right to suspend construction operations if there were a failure to make some payment of a sum due. However, in the majority of situations a decision to suspend the works always carried with it a high risk that the party in breach would treat such suspension as a repudiatory breach. In those circumstances the party in default could purport to accept the breach and sue the other party for damages. The Act provides a powerful remedy to apply commercial pressure for the payment of amounts due under a construction contract by providing a mechanism for suspending performance of the contract.

Section 112(1) provides:

> *"Where a sum due under a construction contract is not paid in full by the final date for payment and no effective notice to withhold payment has been given, the person to whom the sum is due has the right (without prejudice to any other right or remedy) to suspend performance of his obligations under the contract to the party by whom payment ought to have been made ("the party in default")."*

The right to suspend performance does not have to be provided for in a construction contract; it is a statutory right which will override any contrary contractual provision.

The sum due under a construction contract is:

- the amount specified in the notice given in accordance with section 110(2), or

- the amount in the section 110(2) notice *less* the amount in an effective notice to withhold payment in accordance with section 111

- in circumstances where the payer has not served a section 110(2) notice, it cannot be the intention of the Act that no sum is due — therefore, the sum due will be the sum contended for by the payee in accordance with the valuation procedure as part of the adequate mechanism, see section 110(1)(a).

The right to suspend performance arises if the sum due has not been paid in full by the final date for payment, see section 110(1)(b). Therefore, without an effective notice under section 111, any attempt to withhold payment, of an amount by way of a set-off or abatement, will entitle the party to whom the money should be paid to suspend performance of its obligations under the contract. The party who is obliged to make payment under the contract is referred to as the "party in default".

The right to suspend performance of the contract is in addition to any other rights or remedies, which will include those other provisions in Part II of the Act and the relevant construction contract.

Since the right to suspend performance of the contract is a Draconian remedy, the remainder of section 112 sets out a procedure which puts the party in default on notice of the other party's intentions.

Section 112(2) provides:

> *"The right may not be exercised without first giving to the party in default at least seven days' notice of intention to suspend performance, stating the ground or grounds on which it is intended to suspend performance."*

The notice to be given (see also section 115) to the party in default cannot be given before the final date for payment because the right to suspend performance does not arise until after the final date for payment has passed. Any attempt to serve a notice before the final date for payment could not set out the grounds on which it is intended to suspend performance since such grounds would not yet have arisen.

Section 112(2) requires that the notice should include the ground(s) on which it is intended to suspend performance. These will be limited to:

- failure to pay the sum due set out in the notice pursuant to section 110(2) or

- any part thereof or

- the payment determined by the adequate mechanism pursuant to section 110(1)(a) in the absence of a notice pursuant to section 110(2) or

- any part thereof or

- any purported set-off or abatement without an effective notice pursuant to section 111.

Section 112(3) provides:

> *"The right to suspend performance ceases when the party in default makes payment in full of the amount due."*

As soon as the party in default has made a full payment of the amount due, by reference to the notice or notices under sections

Mike,

Please let me know if there are
any problems with these! The
Cwm Bypass 3 emailed to you, these are
the other two. We have copies for our files.

Many Thanks

Jennifer

Mott MacDonald

St Anne House
Wellesley Road
Croydon CR9 2UL
United Kingdom

Telephone +44 (0)20 8774 2000
Fax +44 (0)20 8681 5706
Web www.mottmac.com

With Compliments

110(2) and 111 respectively, the other party must continue with the performance of its obligations under the contract.

A party who has suspended performance of the construction operations and has re-allocated resources or demobilised, to any extent, is at risk of incurring "self-inflicted" delays if full re-commencement of the construction operations is not possible immediately after receiving payment. Consequences for both parties with regard to extensions of time and loss and expense are dealt with below under section 112(4).

Of all the sections in Part II of the Act, section 112 provides the most powerful remedy to bring pressure on a party who is in default of making payment. Section 112(4) provides:

> *"Any period during which performance is suspended in pursuance of the right conferred by this section shall be disregarded in computing for the purposes of any contractual time limit the time taken, by the party exercising the right or by a third party, to complete any work directly or indirectly affected by the exercise of the right.*
>
> *Where the contractual time limit is set by reference to a date rather than a period, the date shall be adjusted accordingly."*

By virtue of this section, the period of time, or the date for completion, of the obligations under the contract is extended by a day for every day such obligations under the contract are suspended. There is of course one overriding proviso — the party exercising its rights of suspension should have complied precisely with the requirements of sections 112(1) and (2). However, this right to a statutory extension to the "contractual time limit" is not limited solely to the party to whom payment is, or was, due.

A third party whose own obligations under a contract (which need not necessarily be a construction contract) are affected, whether directly or indirectly, has the statutory entitlement to benefit from an extension of time equal to the "period during which performance is suspended" by the party to whom the money is, or was, owed.

The third party will have to have had notice of the suspension by another party before it can ascertain whether or not its own obligations have been affected, whether directly or indirectly. A party who has exercised its right to suspend performance of its obligations may be able to maximise its commercial pressure on the party in default by notifying all the other identifiable parties who would be affected, directly or indirectly, by the suspension. The third parties would therefore be in a position to apply for a corresponding extension of time for their own obligations under their own contracts, subject always to the the third parties being prepared to prove that their obligations were affected directly or indirectly.

It is significant that the Act does not require that a third party has to be in contract with the party in default. Therefore, by way of an example, a sub-sub-contractor who suspended its obligations under a contract with sub-contractor A, could entitle sub-contractor B to the same extension, in circumstances where both sub-contractors A and B are working for the same main contractor.

The statutory extension to the "contractual time limit" to complete the construction operations has the effect of postponing the defaulting party's right to recover damages from the party exercising its rights of suspension, for delay or, more generally, liquidated damages. The lost opportunity to recover damages earlier than might otherwise have been the case is unlikely to be the only commercial consequence. The defaulting party may also be liable to its employer in respect of a contract between its employer and a third party who had been able to benefit from an extension of time. There may be a further liability for the defaulting party, depending on the terms of the construction contract, for loss and expense incurred by the party exercising its right of suspension. Legitimate loss and expense would include the costs of maintaining a site establishment during the period of a suspension, or costs of demobilisation and subsequent remobilisation. Similarly, liability would be owed by the defaulting party to its employer under the same circumstances where there was a liability for loss of opportunity for it to claim damages or liquidated damages from other contractors.

Many standard forms of contract provide that the contract is determinable by either party in the event that a suspension lasts for longer than a fixed period of time. Thus, it would be possible, depending on the terms of the contract, for a contractor who had been suspending its obligations, in accordance with section 112, beyond a specified period in a construction contract to determine the contract.

The Scheme for Construction Contracts will not affect section 112 since there is no need for any agreement between the parties. However, the terms and conditions of construction contracts may be amended to address the grounds which are acceptable for claiming loss and expense and determining the contract in circumstances where a party exercises its rights under section 112.

Prohibition of conditional payment provisions

The clause found in some construction contracts, prior to the Act, which probably was more criticised and vilified than any other was the so-called "pay when paid" or "pay if paid" clause. A pay when paid clause hurts the party which has supplied goods or services but is not paid because, the recipient which has received the benefit of such goods and services is able to delay payment indefinitely until some other party has made payment to it, either directly or indirectly, in respect of such goods and services.

Sub-contractors were particularly vulnerable to the pay when paid clause because of the lack of bargaining power. The Latham Report[3] agreed with the vociferous representations made by some organisations and recommended that such clauses should be prohibited. Therefore, it is not surprising that the Act provides for the prohibition of pay when paid clauses or, as the Act refers to them, conditional payment provisions, as it refers to them. Therefore, the days when small companies, which make up the bulk of the sub-contracting fraternity, effectively bankroll the larger contractors are over; or are they? Section 113(1) provides:

> *"A provision making payment under a construction contract conditional on the payer receiving payment from a third person is ineffective, unless that third person, or any other person payment by whom is under the contract (directly or indirectly) a condition of payment by that third person, is insolvent."*

Section 113(1) has no effect on the parts of a contract which relate to exempt construction operations, which emphasises the need to make a distinction between exempt and non-exempt construction operations. Unless the distinction is clear, or there is an express provision which waives the exemption, there may be difficulties in allocating withholding of payment.

The section has two distinct parts. The first part is quite unequivocal; *"A provision making payment under a construction contract conditional on the payer receiving payment from a third person is ineffective..."*. The third person, most probably, would be identified as the person on whom the payer was relying to make payment before making a payment under the construction contract. It is not necessary for the person expecting to receive payment from the payer to know or understand the relationship between the third person and the payer.

It is interesting to note that the Act uses the word "ineffective" rather than "unenforceable", although it is doubtful whether any argument will turn on this point. If a provision is ineffective, it should not achieve that which one of the parties would desire. The section ensures that the construction contract is not made void or voidable nor upsets other payment conditions which may be difficult to disentangle from conditional payment provisions.

The remedies available to the payee beyond the final date for payment of money due under the contract and notified in accordance with section 110, and subject to section 111, if appropriate, are either:

- give a notice under section 112 to suspend performance and/or

- refer to adjudication and/or

- instigate legal proceedings or arbitration as appropriate.

The second part of the section provides a condition to render conditional payment clauses effective, which are otherwise ineffective, in the circumstances as follows:

- the third person is insolvent, or

- any other person, payment by whom is *under the contract* (directly or indirectly) a condition of payment by that third person, is insolvent.

The third person may be identified in the contract and the "other person" may also be identified in the contract, although it is not necessary that either or both should be so identified. Therefore, in circumstances where B is liable for the payment to A under a construction contract, B can avoid making any payment (subject to such a provision being within the contract) by proving that C, who was due to make a payment to B, had become insolvent. This limitation on the requirement on B to make payment to A is extended further to *any other person* becoming insolvent.

If C is expecting payment from D, before making a payment to B, and D becomes insolvent it is open for C to withhold payment to B (subject to such a provision being in the contract between C and B). B could then refuse to pay A provided that the construction contract recognised that the payment to B by C was dependent upon D remaining solvent. Such a contract provision would be in the following, or similar, form:

"the Sub-Contractor shall not be entitled to payment from the Contractor in the event that the Contractor's employer has

become insolvent before the final date for payment under the contract between the Contractor and its employer or because the Contractor's employer has not received payment from another person (or persons) who has (or have) become insolvent before the final date for payment under the contract between the Contractor's employer and the other person (or persons) and which was a pre-condition of the Contractor's employer making payment to the Contractor."

Such a clause would in many situations be related to works connected with a construction project under each contract, although it is not an express requirement of section 113. Therefore, the contract between C and B in the above example does not have to be an entire construction contract but, by providing a contract clause in similar form throughout a long chain of contracts and sub-contracts, will produce the result that any party within the chain who becomes insolvent leaves the sub-contractor at the bottom of the chain out of pocket.

The precise timing from when it is calculated that a party in the contractual chain has become insolvent may be crucial. The dating of the insolvency event, by reference to section 113(2), (3) or (4) below is a matter of fact. If the insolvency of C occurs after the date for payment under the contract between B and C in circumstances where C owed money to B (which included an element of payment to A), it is unclear whether B is still required to pay A if B has not received any payment. Conversely, if C has paid B but C is insolvent at the time of the final date of payment to A, is B still required to pay A? The spirit of the Act would suggest that B should pay A but construction contracts may clarify the situation such that if B remains unpaid simply because C is insolvent at any time, no money is due to A.

The section is also unclear as to the outcome if one of the parties in the contractual chain was receiving payment from two or more sources. Therefore, if C was obtaining payment from D and E, is B entitled to payment if only D or only E becomes insolvent?

Whether or not the third party or the other person is insolvent is a question of fact.

In respect of incorporated companies, section 113(2) provides:

"For the purposes of this section a company becomes insolvent—

(a)   on the making of an administration order against it under Part II of the Insolvency Act 1986,

(b)   on the appointment of an administrative receiver or a receiver or manager of its property under Chapter I of Part III of that Act, or the appointment of a receiver under Chapter II of that Part,

(c)   on the passing of a resolution for voluntary winding-up without a declaration of solvency under section 89 of that Act, or

(d)   on the making of a winding-up order under Part IV or V of that Act."

In respect of partnerships, section 113(3) provides:

"For the purposes of this section a partnership becomes insolvent—

(a)   on the making of a winding-up order against it under any provision of the Insolvency Act 1986 as applied by an order under section 420 of that Act, or

(b)   when sequestration is awarded on the estate of the partnership under section 12 of the Bankruptcy (Scotland) Act 1985 or the partnership grants a trust deed for its creditors."

In respect of individuals, section 113(4) provides:

"For the purposes of this section an individual becomes insolvent—

(a) on the making of a bankruptcy order against him under Part IX of the Insolvency Act 1986, or

(b) on the sequestration of his estate under the Bankruptcy (Scotland) Act 1985 or when he grants a trust deed for his creditors."

There will be instances when parties to a construction project are not always incorporated or resident in England and Wales, or Scotland, and the question arises how the insolvency provisions apply to such parties. Section 113(5) provides:

"A company, partnership or individual shall also be treated as insolvent on the occurrence of any event corresponding to those specified in subsection (2), (3) or (4) under the law of Northern Ireland or of a country outside the United Kingdom."

To identify an event within a foreign jurisdiction which corresponds to those events specified in subsections (2), (3) or (4) is beyond the scope of this commentary but would, of necessity, require an in-depth understanding of the insolvency law for the particular jurisdiction in which the insolvent party is incorporated or resides.

Pay when paid clauses were not found universally in construction contracts prior to the Act. However, since the Act gives effect to such clauses in the circumstances of insolvency in subsections (2) to (5) it will not be surprising if this encourages a wider adoption of the pay when paid clause to be applied in circumstances of insolvency. Thus, it will still fall to the parties lower down the contractual chain to absorb the losses consequent upon a third party's, or other person's, insolvency.

Section 113(6) provides:

"Where a provision is rendered ineffective by subsection (1), the parties are free to agree other terms for payment.

In the absence of such agreement, the relevant provisions of the Scheme for Construction Contracts apply."

If a pay when paid clause is rendered ineffective, it is difficult to imagine the party expecting to be paid agreeing to some other arrangement whereby the payment would be deferred. However, if such a provision is rendered ineffective and leaves the remaining payment provisions inadequate, the Scheme for Construction Contracts will apply.

A final thought: deprived of the opportunity of relying upon a pay when paid clause, a contractor who suffers late payment can delay payment to a sub-contractor by abusing the provision under section 111 to make dubious allegations entitling the contractor to withhold payment. Such a tactic would buy at least six weeks more time, even if the sub-contractor referred the dispute to adjudication without delay.

Summary of key issues

Section 109
Entitlement to stage payments

- Entitlement to stage payments depends upon whether the duration of the contract works is less or more than 45 days

Section 110
Dates for payment

- What is the adequate mechanism for determining what payments become due and when?

- Agree a period in the contract between the sum becoming due and the final date for payment

- Serve a section 110(2) notice, not later than five days after a payment becomes due, specifying the amount

- Ensure that the section 110(2) notice complies with all the requirements of section 110(2) on the basis that the payee has complied with all its obligations and no deduction is made for set-off or abatement

Section 111
Notice of intention to withhold payment

- A notice to withhold payment must be served before deducting any sum from the payment due under the section 110(2) notice

- Ensure that the section 110(2) notice is served no later than a prescribed period before the final date for payment

- Consider the appropriate length of time for the prescribed period and include this within the contract

- Consider including the requirements of the section 111 notice within a section 110(2) notice

- Ensure that each and every ground for deducting money is identified, together with the amount attributable to each ground

- Consider making provision in the contract for payment of any sum awarded by the adjudicator within seven days of the decision or the final date for payment, whichever is the later

Section 112
Right to suspend performance for non-payment

- The right to suspend performance does not have to be provided for in the contract
- Strict compliance with the notice requirements is necessary before exercising the right of suspension including seven days notice and grounds of complaint
- Consider the full extent of liability of payer to its employer and the payee for reimbursement for loss and expense and entitlement to liquidated damages
- Consider making provision for determination of the contract if the period of suspension exceeds a specified length of time

Section 113
Prohibition of conditional payment provisions

- Pay when paid clauses are effective in the event of a third party, or other person, becoming insolvent as provided for by section 113(1)
- Does the insolvency of a third party, or other person, after a final date for payment in the relevant contract come within the Act to render a conditional payment clause ineffective if the payer still has not received payment? — the precise date of insolvency may be crucial
- The insolvency of a party not incorporated in England and Wales or Scotland will be construed in accordance with the local law of the place where that party is incorporated or resident

Generally:

- Ensure that contracts and sub-contracts have compatible time periods for all the payment provisions

6 The Scheme for Construction Contracts

Section 114(1) to (3) provides:

> *"(1) The Minister shall by regulations make a scheme ("the Scheme for Construction Contracts") containing provision about the matters referred to in the preceding provisions of this Part.*
>
> *(2) Before making any regulations under this section the Minister shall consult such persons as he thinks fit.*
>
> *(3) In this section "the Minister" means—*
>
> *(a) for England and Wales, the Secretary of State, and*
>
> *(b) for Scotland, the Lord Advocate."*

The Secretary of State and the Lord Advocate commenced the consultation process pursuant to the first commencement order made under section 150(3) which provided the necessary authority to consult under section 114(2).[7]

The need for a separate Scheme for Construction Contracts in England and Wales and for Scotland arises from the different judicial systems.

The Scheme for Construction Contracts will be in two parts which will include provisions with regard to:

Part 1 — Adjudication

- the adjudication procedure under section 108

Part 2 — Payments

- the entitlement to stage payments under section 109

- an adequate mechanism for determining what payments become due under section 110(1)(a)

- the final date for payments under section 110(1)(b)

- giving of a notice in accordance with section 110(2)

- the prescribed period for serving a notice of intention to withhold payment before the final date under section 111

- terms of payment if a pay when paid clause is ineffective under section 113.

Section 114(4) provides:

> *"Where any provisions of the Scheme for Construction Contracts apply by virtue of this Part in default of contractual provision agreed by the parties, they have effect as implied terms of the contract concerned."*

Terms can be implied into contracts which, the parties have expressly adopted, derived either from custom and usage, the courts, or statute. The implied terms in construction contracts based on custom and usage supplement other express terms. Typically some implied terms might include warranties to co-operate, not to prevent completion or the use of proper skill and care. Other terms implied by the courts are to give a contract business efficacy in circumstances where, unless a term is implied, the contract is robbed of any commercial sense. However, terms implied by statute may achieve both these objectives and more, for reasons of policy — and so it is with the Scheme for Construction Contracts.

One of the best examples of terms of a contract being implied by statute is the Sale of Goods Act 1979. When the first Sale of Goods Act of 1893 was enacted, it was substantially a codification of the common law of sale. The Sale of Goods Act implied terms into contracts for the sale of goods, many of which are to be applied unless the parties provide otherwise. Prior to the codification of the area of common law governing the sale of goods, the implied terms were those which the courts had accepted as necessary based on commercial practice and usage. The Supply of Goods and Services Act 1982 is directly applicable to construction contracts and implies terms dealing with reasonable care and skill, reasonable time and a reasonable charge.

The Scheme for Construction Contracts will provide those terms which the parties should have agreed in accordance with the Act but have omitted to do so. But, the terms that will be implied by the Scheme for Construction Contracts will not be based on usage or custom but on the views of the Secretary of State of what is best for parties to a construction contract, albeit that the Secretary of State will have consulted with such persons as he thinks fit, as referred to in section 114(2).

Section 114(5) provides:

> *"Regulations under this section shall not be made unless a draft of them has been approved by resolution of each House of Parliament."*

Part II of the Act will not come into full force until such time as the Scheme for Construction Contracts has been so approved.

7 Miscellaneous

Service of notices

The operation of Part II of the Act relies on the service of notices if the parties to a construction contract are to preserve the rights and protection which are central to the original intent of the legislature.

The content and timing of different notices are dealt with in the preceding sections, save for a notice to refer a dispute to adjudication. Crucial to ensuring that a notice is effective is the need for some rules as to how a notice should be served and when service has taken place. Section 115(1) deals with these issues.

Section 115(1) provides:

> *"The parties are free to agree on the manner of service of any notice or other document required or authorised to be served in pursuance of the construction contract or for any of the purposes of this Part."*

Thus, the parties are free to agree the manner of service of notices required by the Act and any other documents required by the terms and conditions of the agreed construction contract. The parties are also free to agree the time from when service is effective. However, in the event that the construction contract does not provide for service of notices or other documents, and in the absence of any subsequent agreement, the remainder of section 115 applies by virtue of section 115(2), which provides:

> *"If or to the extent that there is no such agreement the following provisions apply."*

The "following provisions" are not comprehensive and there is no reference to finding relevant provisions in the Scheme for Construction Contracts.

Section 115(3) provides:

> *"A notice or other document may be served on a person by any effective means."*

"Person" in the context of section 115(3) is either an individual, a partnership, a company incorporated in England, Wales or Scotland or a company incorporated abroad.

A notice, or other document, served by "any effective means" will not be satisfied by an oral communication because the recipient must have possession of the "notice or other document". However, the means available to effect service include:

- personal service

- telex

- fax

- electronic mail

- courier service

- first or second class post

- recorded delivery

- registered post.

To be effective, the party serving the notice must be able to prove that the other party actually received the notice or document. To avoid the uncertainty to the party serving the notice or document as to whether it has been received, the Act provides for the presumption of effective service by post. Section 115(4) provides:

> *"If a notice or other document is addressed, pre-paid and delivered by post—*
>
> *(a) to the addressee's last known principal residence or, if he is or has been carrying on a trade, profession or business, his last known principal business address, or*
>
> *(b) where the addressee is a body corporate, to the body's registered or principal office,*
>
> *it shall be treated as effectively served."*

Subsection 115(4) does not specify whether the postage should be first or second class. At the present time, while the Post Office still enjoys a monopoly, there is no distinction between first-class and second-class post for the purposes of effective service. Thus, a party on whom a notice has been served by first-class or second-class post cannot deny, save in exceptional circumstances, having received the notice or document. Because the time of delivery for first-class and second-class post is different, the time when service is effected will be different. The Act does not assist because it does not specify whether postage should be first class or second class. There is also no reference to assistance from the Scheme for Construction Contracts. The date from which service is deemed to have taken place will either be a matter of fact when service was effected or in accordance with a prior agreement.

Determining the date from which service is effected should not be underestimated because the time limits in the preceding sections are expressed in days only, either five or seven. Both parties can be at risk from failing to serve or respond to the service of notices within the relevant time limits.

Section 115(5) provides:

> *"This section does not apply to the service of documents for the purposes of legal proceedings, for which provision is made by rules of court."*

The service of documents for the purpose of legal proceedings does not include arbitration or adjudication. Legal proceedings are governed by the rules of the Supreme Court[8] or the county court rules[9].

By contrast with the provisions of subsections 115(3) and (4), service of documents in legal proceedings is defined precisely. For instance, postal service is only effective if it is pre-paid and sent by first-class post. The time of service is dealt with in detail within the rules of court[8,9] and depends upon the identity of the person being served and the means of service. Some, if not all, of the rules of service in legal proceedings could be adopted without difficulty within construction contracts with the advantage of defining the consequences of the chosen methods of service of notices or other documents with regard to establishing the actual time of service.

Section 115(6) provides:

> *"References in this Part to a notice or other document include any form of communication in writing and references to service shall be construed accordingly."*

This subsection establishes, for the avoidance of doubt, that notices or other documents can be in any form of writing (cross-refer to section 107(6)) and therefore section 115 is to be construed accordingly.

Reckoning periods of time

Part II of the Act specifies periods of time in days. Not all days count for the purposes of reckoning time. Section 116 provides:

> *"(1) For the purposes of this Part periods of time shall be reckoned as follows.*
>
> *(2) Where an act is required to be done within a specified period after or from a specified date, the period begins immediately after that date.*
>
> *(3) Where the period would include Christmas Day, Good Friday or a day which under the Banking and Financial Dealings Act 1971 is a bank holiday in England and Wales or, as the case may be, in Scotland, that day shall be excluded."*

It is important for the purposes of construing subsection 116(3) that the parties are aware of the date from which service has been effected. Close attention to *when* notices are served effectively is dealt with in the preceding commentary on section 115. It should be noted that Saturdays and Sundays are not excluded for the purposes of reckoning time. Therefore, without a prior agreement, service can take place on a Saturday or a Sunday, with time beginning to run from the following day. In particular, note that the five-day period in section 110(2) can include a weekend, thus only providing three normal working days of time within which to serve the notice.

Crown application

Section 117(1) provides:

> *"This Part applies to the construction contract entered into by or on behalf of the Crown otherwise than by or on behalf of Her Majesty in her private capacity."*

The Queen, contracting in her private capacity, is not subject to the provisions of Part II of the Act although Her Majesty's Government, which acts in the name of the Crown and includes government departments and the armed forces, are so subject.

Section 117(2) provides:

"This Part applies to a construction contract entered into on behalf of the Duchy of Cornwall notwithstanding any Crown interest."

The Duchy of Cornwall is one of the estates vested in the Prince of Wales by virtue of his being the Duke of Cornwall. Any construction contract with the Duchy of Cornwall is subject to the provisions of Part II of the Act.

Section 117(3) provides:

"Where a construction contract is entered into by or on behalf of Her Majesty in right of the Duchy of Lancaster, Her Majesty shall be represented, for the purposes of any adjudication or other proceedings arising out of the contract by virtue of this Part, by the Chancellor of the Duchy or such person as he may appoint."

The Duchy of Lancaster is one of the estates vested in the Queen. Any construction contract with the Duchy of Lancaster is subject to the provisions of Part II of the Act. The representative of the Duchy of Lancaster is the Chancellor of the Duchy, for the purposes of administering the construction contract, or any such person as the Chancellor of the Duchy may appoint.

Section 117(4) provides:

"Where a construction contract is entered into on behalf of the Duchy of Cornwall, the Duke of Cornwall or the possessor for the time being of the Duchy shall be represented, for the purposes of any adjudication or other proceedings arising out of the contract by virtue of this Part, by such person as he may appoint."

The Prince of Wales, or his successor, shall be represented by a person appointed by him as the Duke of Cornwall for the purposes of adjudication or other proceedings.

Orders, regulations and directions

Part II of the Act has a number of provisions which allow for later amendments and the introduction of the Scheme for Construction Contracts. Such is the importance or potential consequences for some categories of amendments and the Scheme for Construction Contracts that *each* House of Parliament is required to scrutinise the provision of the proposed amendments and the Scheme. Thus, the draft Order has to be laid before and approved by an affirmation resolution of the House of Commons *and* the House of Lords. Those matters which require an affirmative resolution of both Houses of Parliament are:

section 104(4) — definition of a construction contract

section 105(4) — amendment to the scope and extent of "construction operations"

section 106(4) — amendment to the exemption from Part II of the Act in respect of residential occupiers and any other description of construction contract as considered necessary by the Secretary of State

section 114(5) — making of the Scheme for Construction Contracts.

In other cases the Secretary of State can make orders to amend the Act by virtue of section 146 without any scrutiny of either House of Parliament.

Appendix 1 Specimen form of referral to adjudication

In the matter of:

Contract dated [   ]

Between:

      [   ] Claimant

           and

      [   ] Respondent

for [description of the construction operations]

Notice to refer to adjudication

TAKE NOTICE that the Claimant pursuant to Section 108 of the Housing Grants, Construction and Regeneration Act 1996 refers the dispute concerning [describe circumstances] to adjudication.

The Claimant proposes that the named persons appearing in the list hereunder are suitable persons to act as adjudicator and invites the Respondent to concur in the appointment of one person appearing in the list;

1.   [Name]: [Qualifications]
        [Address]

2.   [Name]: [Qualifications]
        [Address]

3.   [Name]: [Qualifications]
        [Address]

Appendix 2 Part II: Housing Grants, Construction and Regeneration Act 1996

The text of Part II of the Housing Grants, Construction and Regeneration Act 1996 is reproduced below.

Part II Construction contracts

Introductory provisions

104 Construction contracts

(1) In this Part a "construction contract" means an agreement with a person for any of the following—

(a) the carrying out of construction operations;

(b) arranging for the carrying out of construction operations by others, whether under sub-contract to him or otherwise;

(c) providing his own labour, or the labour of others, for the carrying out of construction operations.

(2) References in this Part to a construction contract include an agreement—

(a) to do architectural, design, or surveying work, or

(b) to provide advice on building, engineering, interior or exterior decoration or on the laying-out of landscape,

in relation to construction operations.

(3)   References in this Part to a construction contract do not include a contract of employment (within the meaning of the Employment Rights Act 1996).

(4)   The Secretary of State may by order add to, amend or repeal any of the provisions of subsection (1), (2) or (3) as to the agreements which are construction contracts for the purposes of this Part or are to be taken or not to be taken as included in references to such contracts.

No such order shall be made unless a draft of it has been laid before and approved by a resolution of each of [sic] House of Parliament.

(5)   Where an agreement relates to construction operations and other matters, this Part applies to it only so far as it relates to construction operations.

An agreement relates to construction operations so far as it makes provision of any kind within subsection (1) or (2).

(6)   This Part applies only to construction contracts which—

(a)   are entered into after the commencement of this Part, and

(b)   relate to the carrying out of construction operations in England, Wales or Scotland.

(7)   This Part applies whether or not the law of England and Wales or Scotland is otherwise the applicable law in relation to the contract.

105 Meaning of "construction operations"

(1)   In this Part "construction operations" means, subject as follows, operations of any of the following descriptions—

(a) construction, alteration, repair, maintenance, extension, demolition or dismantling of buildings, or structures forming, or to form, part of the land (whether permanent or not);

(b) construction, alteration, repair, maintenance, extension, demolition or dismantling of any works forming, or to form, part of the land, including (without prejudice to the foregoing) walls, roadworks, power-lines, telecommunication apparatus, aircraft runways, docks and harbours, railways, inland waterways, pipe-lines, reservoirs, water-mains, wells, sewers, industrial plant and installations for purposes of land drainage, coast protection or defence;

(c) installation in any building or structure of fittings forming part of the land, including (without prejudice to the foregoing) systems of heating, lighting, air-conditioning, ventilation, power supply, drainage, sanitation, water supply or fire protection, or security or communications systems;

(d) external or internal cleaning of buildings and structures, so far as carried out in the course of their construction, alteration, repair, extension or restoration;

(e) operations which form an integral part of, or are preparatory to, or are for rendering complete, such operations as are previously described in this subsection, including site clearance, earth-moving, excavation, tunnelling and boring, laying of foundations, erection, maintenance or dismantling of scaffolding, site restoration, landscaping and the provision of roadways and other access works;

(f) painting or decorating the internal or external surfaces of any building or structure.

(2) The following operations are not construction operations within the meaning of this Part—

(a) drilling for, or extraction of, oil or natural gas;

(b) extraction (whether by underground or surface working) of minerals; tunnelling or boring, or construction of underground works, for this purpose;

(c) assembly, installation or demolition of plant or machinery, or erection or demolition of steelwork for the purposes of supporting or providing access to plant or machinery, on a site where the primary activity is—

(i) nuclear processing, power generation, or water or effluent treatment, or

(ii) the production, transmission, processing or bulk storage (other than warehousing) of chemicals, pharmaceuticals, oil, gas, steel or food and drink;

(d) manufacture or delivery to site of—

(i) building or engineering components or equipment,

(ii) materials, plant or machinery, or

(iii) components for systems of heating, lighting, air-conditioning, ventilation, power supply, drainage, sanitation, water supply or fire protection, or for security or communications systems,

except under a contract which also provides for their installation;

(e) the making, installation and repair of artistic works, being sculptures, murals and other works which are wholly artistic in nature.

(3) The Secretary of State may by order add to, amend or repeal any of the provisions of subsection (1) or (2) as to the operations and work to be treated as construction operations for the purposes of this Part.

(4) No such order shall be made unless a draft of it has been laid before and approved by a resolution of each House of Parliament.

106 Provisions not applicable to contract with residential occupier

(1) This Part does not apply—

(a) to a construction contract with a residential occupier (see below), or

(b) to any other description of construction contract excluded from the operation of this Part by order of the Secretary of State.

(2) A construction contract with a residential occupier means a construction contract which principally relates to operations on a dwelling which one of the parties to the contract occupies, or intends to occupy, as his residence.

In this subsection "dwelling" means a dwelling-house or a flat; and for this purpose—

"dwelling-house" does not include a building containing a flat; and

"flat" means separate and self-contained premises constructed or adapted for use for residential purposes and forming part of a building from some other part of which the premises are divided horizontally.

(3) The Secretary of State may by order amend subsection (2).

(4) No order under this section shall be made unless a draft of it has been laid before and approved by a resolution of each House of Parliament.

107 Provisions applicable only to agreements in writing

(1) The provisions of this Part apply only where the construction contract is in writing, and any other agreement between the parties as to any matter is effective for the purposes of this Part only if in writing.

The expressions "agreement", "agree" and "agreed" shall be construed accordingly.

(2) There is an agreement in writing—

(a) if the agreement is made in writing (whether or not it is signed by the parties),

(b) if the agreement is made by exchange of communications in writing, or

(c) if the agreement is evidenced in writing.

(3) Where parties agree otherwise than in writing by reference to terms which are in writing, they make an agreement in writing.

(4) An agreement is evidenced in writing if an agreement made otherwise than in writing is recorded by one of the parties, or by a third party, with the authority of the parties to the agreement.

(5) An exchange of written submissions in adjudication proceedings, or in arbitral or legal proceedings in which the
existence of an agreement otherwise than in writing is
alleged by one party against another party and not denied
by the other party in his response constitutes as between
those parties an agreement in writing to the effect alleged.

(6) References in this Part to anything being written or in
writing include its being recorded by any means.

Adjudication

108 Right to refer disputes to adjudication

(1) A party to a construction contract has the right to refer a
dispute arising under the contract for adjudication under
a procedure complying with this section.

For this purpose "dispute" includes any difference.

(2) The contract shall—

(a) enable a party to give notice at any time of his
intention to refer a dispute to adjudication;

(b) provide a timetable with the object of securing the
appointment of the adjudicator and referral of the
dispute to him within 7 days of such notice;

(c) require the adjudicator to reach a decision within 28
days of referral or such longer period as is agreed by
the parties after the dispute was referred;

(d) allow the adjudicator to extend the period of 28 days
by up to 14 days, with the consent of the party by
whom the dispute was referred;

(e) impose a duty on the adjudicator to act impartially;
and

(f) enable the adjudicator to take the initiative in ascertaining the facts and the law.

(3) The contract shall provide that the decision of the adjudicator is binding until the dispute is finally determined by legal proceedings, by arbitration (if the contract provides for arbitration or the parties otherwise agree to arbitration) or by agreement.

The parties may agree to accept the decision of the adjudicator as finally determining the dispute.

(4) The contract shall also provide that the adjudicator is not liable for anything done or omitted in the discharge or purported discharge of his functions as adjudicator unless the act or omission is in bad faith, and that any employee or agent of the adjudicator is similarly protected from liability.

(5) If the contract does not comply with the requirements of subsections (1) to (4), the adjudication provisions of the Scheme for Construction Contracts apply.

(6) For England and Wales, the Scheme may apply the provisions of the Arbitration Act 1996 with such adaptations and modifications as appear to the Minister making the scheme to be appropriate.

For Scotland, the Scheme may include provision conferring powers on courts in relation to adjudication and provision relating to the enforcement of the adjudicator's decisions.

Payment
109 Entitlement to stage payments

(1) A party to a construction contract is entitled to payment by instalments, stage payments or other periodic payments for any work under the contract unless—

(a) it is specified in the contract that the duration of the work is to be less than 45 days, or

(b) it is agreed between the parties that the duration of the work is estimated to be less than 45 days.

(2) The parties are free to agree the amounts of the payments and the intervals at which, or circumstances in which, they become due.

(3) In the absence of such agreement, the relevant provisions of the Scheme for Construction Contracts apply.

(4) References in the following sections to a payment under the contract include a payment by virtue of this section.

110 Dates for payment

(1) Every construction contract shall—

(a) provide an adequate mechanism for determining what payments become due under the contract, and when, and

(b) provide for a final date for payment in relation to any sum which becomes due.

The parties are free to agree how long the period is to be between the date on which a sum becomes due and the final date for payment.

(2) Every construction contract shall provide for the giving of notice by a party not later than five days after the date on which a payment becomes due from him under the contract, or would have become due if—

(a) the other party had carried out his obligations under the contract, and

(b) no set-off or abatement was permitted by reference to any sum claimed to be due under one or more other contracts,

specifying the amount (if any) of the payment made or proposed to be made, and the basis on which that amount was calculated.

(3) If or to the extent that a contract does not contain such provision as is mentioned in subsection (1) or (2), the relevant provisions of the Scheme for Construction Contracts apply.

111 Notice of intention to withhold payment

(1) A party to a construction contract may not withhold payment after the final date for payment of a sum due under the contract unless he has given an effective notice of intention to withhold payment.

The notice mentioned in section 110(2) may suffice as a notice of intention to withhold payment if it complies with the requirements of this section.

(2) To be effective such a notice must specify—

(a) the amount proposed to be withheld and the ground for withholding payment, or

   (b) if there is more than one ground, each ground and the amount attributable to it,

and must be given not later than the prescribed period before the final date for payment.

(3)   The parties are free to agree what that prescribed period is to be.

In the absence of such agreement, the period shall be that provided by the Scheme for Construction Contracts.

(4)   Where an effective notice of intention to withhold payment is given, but on the matter being referred to adjudication it is decided that the whole or part of the amount should be paid, the decision shall be construed as requiring payment not later than—

   (a) seven days from the date of the decision, or

   (b) the date which apart from the notice would have been the final date for payment,

whichever is the later.

12 Right to suspend performance for non-payment

(1)   Where a sum due under a construction contract is not paid in full by the final date for payment and no effective notice to withhold payment has been given, the person to whom the sum is due has the right (without prejudice to any other right or remedy) to suspend performance of his obligations under the contract to the party by whom payment ought to have been made ("the party in default").

(2)   The right may not be exercised without first giving to the party in default at least seven days' notice of intention to

suspend performance, stating the ground or grounds on which it is intended to suspend performance.

(3) The right to suspend performance ceases when the party in default makes payment in full of the amount due.

(4) Any period during which performance is suspended in pursuance of the right conferred by this section shall be disregarded in computing for the purposes of any contractual time limit the time taken, by the party exercising the right or by a third party, to complete any work directly or indirectly affected by the exercise of the right.

Where the contractual time limit is set by reference to a date rather than a period, the date shall be adjusted accordingly.

113 Prohibition of conditional payment provisions

(1) A provision making payment under a construction contract conditional on the payer receiving payment from a third person is ineffective, unless that third person, or any other person payment by whom is under the contract (directly or indirectly) a condition of payment by that third person, is insolvent.

(2) For the purposes of this section a company becomes insolvent—

(a) on the making of an administration order against it under Part II of the Insolvency Act 1986,

(b) on the appointment of an administrative receiver or a receiver or manager of its property under Chapter I of Part III of that Act, or the appointment of a receiver under Chapter II of that Part,

(c) on the passing of a resolution for voluntary winding-up without a declaration of solvency under section 89 of that Act, or

(d) on the making of a winding-up order under Part IV or V of that Act.

(3) For the purposes of this section a partnership becomes insolvent—

(a) on the making of a winding-up order against it under any provision of the Insolvency Act 1986 as applied by an order under section 420 of that Act, or

(b) when sequestration is awarded on the estate of the partnership under section 12 of the Bankruptcy (Scotland) Act 1985 or the partnership grants a trust deed for its creditors.

(4) For the purposes of this section an individual becomes insolvent—

(a) on the making of a bankruptcy order against him under Part IX of the Insolvency Act 1986, or

(b) on the sequestration of his estate under the Bankruptcy (Scotland) Act 1985 or when he grants a trust deed for his creditors.

(5) A company, partnership or individual shall also be treated as insolvent on the occurrence of any event corresponding to those specified in subsection (2), (3) or (4) under the law of Northern Ireland or of a country outside the United Kingdom.

(6) Where a provision is rendered ineffective by subsection (1), the parties are free to agree other terms for payment.

In the absence of such agreement, the relevant provisions of the Scheme for Construction Contracts apply.˙

Supplementary provisions

114 The Scheme for Construction Contracts

(1) The Minister shall by regulations make a scheme ("the Scheme for Construction Contracts") containing provision about the matters referred to in the preceding provisions of the Part.

(2) Before making any regulations under this section the Minister shall consult such persons as he thinks fit.

(3) In this section "the Minister" means—

   (a) for England and Wales, the Secretary of State, and

   (b) for Scotland, the Lord Advocate.

(4) Where any provisions of the Scheme for Construction Contracts apply by virtue of this Part in default of contractual provision agreed by the parties, they have effect as implied terms of the contract concerned.

(5) Regulations under this section shall not be made unless a draft of them has been approved by resolution of each House of Parliament.

115 Service of notices, &c

(1) The parties are free to agree on the manner of service of any notice or other document required or authorised to be served in pursuance of the construction contract or for any of the purposes of this Part.

(2) If or to the extent that there is no such agreement the following provisions apply.

(3) A notice or other document may be served on a person by any effective means.

(4) If a notice or other document is addressed, pre-paid and delivered by post—

   (a) to the addressee's last known principal residence or, if he is or has been carrying on a trade, profession or business, his last known principal business address, or

   (b) where the addressee is a body corporate, to the body's registered or principal office,

   it shall be treated as effectively served.

(5) This section does not apply to the service of documents for the purposes of legal proceedings, for which provision is made by rules of court.

(6) References in this Part to a notice or other document include any form of communication in writing and references to service shall be construed accordingly.

116 Reckoning periods of time

(1) For the purposes of this Part periods of time shall be reckoned as follows.

(2) Where an act is required to be done within a specified period after or from a specified date, the period begins immediately after that date.

(3) Where the period would include Christmas Day, Good Friday or a day which under the Banking and Financial

Dealings Act 1971 is a bank holiday in England and Wales or, as the case may be, in Scotland, that day shall be excluded.

117 Crown application

(1) This Part applies to a construction contract entered into by or on behalf of the Crown otherwise than by or on behalf of Her Majesty in her private capacity.

(2) This Part applies to a construction contract entered into on behalf of the Duchy of Cornwall notwithstanding any Crown interest.

(3) Where a construction contract is entered into by or on behalf of Her Majesty in right of the Duchy of Lancaster, Her Majesty shall be represented, for the purposes of any adjudication or other proceedings arising out of the contract by virtue of this Part, by the Chancellor of the Duchy or such person as he may appoint.

(4) Where a construction contract is entered into on behalf of the Duchy of Cornwall, the Duke of Cornwall or the possessor for the time being of the Duchy shall be represented, for the purposes of any adjudication or other proceedings arising out of the contract by virtue of this Part, by such person as he may appoint.

Source: The Housing Grants, Construction and Regeneration Act 1996. HMSO, London, 1996.

Appendix 3 Definition of "construction work"

Regulation 2(1) of the Construction (Design and Management) Regulations 1994 defines "construction work" as:

> *"the carrying out of any building, civil engineering or engineering construction work and includes any of the following:*
>
> *(a) the construction, alteration, conversion, fitting out, commissioning, renovation, repair, upkeep, redecoration or other maintenance (including cleaning which involves the use of water or an abrasive at high pressure or the use of substance classified as corrosive or toxic for the purposes of Regulation 7 of the Chemicals (Hazard Information and Packing) Regulations 1993) decommissioning, demolition or dismantling of a structure;*
>
> *(b) the preparation for an intended structure including site clearance, exploration, investigation (but not site survey) and excavation, and laying or installing the foundations of the structure;*
>
> *(c) the assembly of prefabricated elements to form a structure or the disassembly of prefabricated elements which, immediately before such disassembly, formed a structure;*
>
> *(d) the removal of a structure or part of a structure or of any product or waste resulting from demolition or dismantling of a structure or from disassembly of pre-fabricated*

elements which, immediately before such disassembly, formed a structure;

(e) the installation, commissioning, maintenance, repair or removal of mechanical, electrical, gas, compressed air, hydraulic, telecommunications, computer or similar services which are normally fixed within or to a structure;

but does not include the exploration for or extraction of mineral resources or activities preparatory thereto carried out in a place where such exploration or extraction is carried out."

The definition of construction work cannot be appreciated fully without a knowledge of the term "structure" which is defined as:

"(a) any building, railway line or siding, tramway line, dock, harbour, inland navigation, tunnel, shaft, bridge, viaduct, waterworks, reservoir, pipe or pipe-line (whatever, in either case, it contains or is intended to contain), cable, aqueduct, sewer, sewage works, gas holder, road, airfield, sea defence works, river works, drainage works, earthworks, lagoon, dam, wall, caisson, mast, tower, pylon, underground tank, earth retaining structure, all structures designed to preserve or alter any natural feature, and any other structure similar to the foregoing;

(b) any formwork, falseworks, scaffold or other structure designed or used to provide support or means of access during construction work;

(c) any fixed plant in respect of work which is installation, commissioning, de-commissioning or dismantling and where any such work involves a risk of a person falling more than two metres."

Appendix 4 Definition of "arrange" and "arranges"

Regulation 2(2) of the Construction (Design and Management) Regulations 1994 defines "arranges" as follows:

> *"In determining whether any person arranges for a person (in this paragraph called "the relevant person") to prepare a design or to carry out or manage construction work regard shall be had to the following, namely—*
>
> *(a) a person does arrange for the relevant person to do a thing where -*
>
> > *(i) he specifies in or in connection with any arrangement with a third person that the relevant person shall do that thing (whether by nominating the relevant person as a subcontractor to the third person or otherwise);*
> >
> > *(ii) being an employer, it is done by any of his employees in-house.*
>
> *(b) A person does not arrange for the relevant person to do a thing where -*
>
> > *(i) being a self-employed person, he does it himself or, being in partnership it is done by any of this partners; or*
> >
> > *(ii) being an employer, it is done by any of his employees otherwise than in-house; or*

      (iii) being a firm carrying on its business anywhere in Great Britain whose principal place of business is in Scotland, it is done by any partner in the firm; or

      (iv) having arranged for a third person to do the thing, he does not object to the third person arranging for it to be done by the relevant person;

and the expressions "arrange" and "arranges" shall be construed accordingly."

Appendix 5 ORSA adjudication rules

The Official Referees Solicitors Association Procedural Rules for Adjudication 1996 Edition v1.1

1. The following Rules

    (i)   may be incorporated into any contract by reference to the "ORSA Adjudication Rules", which expression shall mean, in relation to any adjudication, the most recent edition hereof as at the date of the written notice requiring that adjudication.

    (ii) meet the requirements of adjudication procedure as set out in section 108 of the Housing Grants, Construction and Regeneration Act 1996; Part I of the Scheme for Construction Contracts shall thus not apply.

Definitions

2. In these Rules:-

"Contract" means the agreement which includes the agreement to adjudicate in accordance with these Rules

"Party" means any party to the Contract

"Chairman of ORSA" means the Chairman for the time being of the Official Referees Solicitors Association, or such other officer thereof as is authorised to deputise for him.

Commencement

3.   These Rules shall apply upon any Party giving written notice to any other Party requiring adjudication, and identifying in general terms the dispute in respect of which adjudication is required.

4.   Such notice may be given at any time and notwithstanding that arbitration or litigation has been commenced in respect of such dispute.

5.   More than one such notice may be given arising out of the same contract.

Appointment

6.   Where the Parties have agreed upon the identity of an adjudicator who confirms his readiness and willingness to embark upon the Adjudication within 7 days of referral to him, then that person shall be the Adjudicator.

7.   Where the Parties have not so agreed upon an adjudicator, or where such person has not so confirmed his willingness to act, then any Party may apply to the Chairman of ORSA for a nomination. The following procedure shall apply:-

(i)   The application shall be in writing, accompanied by a copy of the Contract or other evidence of the agreement of the Parties that these Rules should apply, a copy of the written notice requiring adjudication, and ORSA's appointment fee of £100.

(ii)   The Chairman of ORSA shall endeavour to secure the appointment of an Adjudicator and the referral to him of the dispute within 7 days from the notice requiring adjudication.

(iii) Any person so appointed, and not any person named in the Contract whose readiness or willingness is in question, shall be the Adjudicator.

8. The Chairman of ORSA shall have the power by written notice to the Parties to replace the Adjudicator with another nominated person if and when it appears necessary to him to do so. The Chairman of ORSA shall consider whether to exercise such power if any Party shall represent to him that the Adjudicator is not acting impartially, or that the Adjudicator is physically or mentally incapable of conducting the Adjudication, or that the Adjudicator is failing with necessary dispatch to proceed with the Adjudication or make his decision. In the event of a replacement under this Rule, directions and decisions of the previous Adjudicator shall remain in effect unless reviewed and replaced by the new Adjudicator, and all timescales shall be recalculated from the date of the replacement.

9. Where an adjudicator has already been appointed in relation to another dispute arising out of the Contract, the Chairman of ORSA may appoint either the same or a different person as Adjudicator.

Agreement

10. An agreement to adjudicate in accordance with these Rules shall be treated as an offer made by each of the Parties to ORSA and to any Adjudicator to abide by these Rules, which offer may be accepted by conduct by appointing an Adjudicator or embarking upon the Adjudication respectively.

Scope of the Adjudication

11. The scope of the Adjudication shall be the matters identified in the notice requiring adjudication, together with

(i)   any further matters which all Parties agree should be within the scope of the Adjudication, and

(ii)   any further matters which the Adjudicator determines must be included in order that the Adjudication may be effective and/or meaningful.

12.   The Adjudicator may rule upon his own substantive jurisdiction, and as to the scope of the Adjudication.

The purpose of the Adjudication and the Role of the Adjudicator

13.   The underlying purpose of the Adjudication is to resolve disputes between the Parties that are within the scope of the Adjudication as rapidly and economically as is reasonably possible.

14.   Decisions of the Adjudicator shall be binding until the dispute is finally determined by legal proceedings, by arbitration (if the Contract provides for arbitration or the parties otherwise agree to arbitration) or by agreement.

15.   Wherever possible, the decision of the Adjudicator shall reflect the legal entitlements of the Parties. Where it appears to the Adjudicator impractical to reach a concluded view upon the legal entitlements of the Parties within the practical constraints of a rapid and economical adjudication process, his decision shall represent his fair and commercially reasonable view of how the disputed matter should lie unless and until resolved by litigation or arbitration.

16.   The Adjudicator shall have the like power to open up and review any certificates or other things issued or made pursuant to the Contract as would an arbitrator appointed pursuant to the Contract and/or a court.

17.   The Adjudicator shall act fairly and impartially, but shall not be obliged or empowered to act as though he were an arbitrator.

Conduct of the Adjudication

18.   The Adjudicator shall establish the procedure and timetable for the Adjudication.

19.   Without prejudice to the generality of Rule 18, the Adjudicator may if he thinks fit:-

(i)   Require the delivery of written statements of case,

(ii)   Require any party to produce a bundle of key documents, whether helpful or otherwise to that Party's case, and to draw such inference as may seem proper from any imbalance in such bundle that may become apparent,

(iii) Require the delivery to him and/or the other parties of copies of any documents other than documents that would be privileged from production to a court,

(iv)   Limit the length of any written or oral submission,

(v)   Require the attendance before him for questioning of any Party or employee or agent of any Party,

(vi)   Make site visits,

(vii) Make use of his own specialist knowledge,

(viii) Obtain advice from specialist consultants, provided that at least one of the Parties so requests or consents,

(ix)   Meet and otherwise communicate with any Party without the presence of other Parties,

(x) Make directions for the conduct of the Adjudication orally or in writing,

(xi) Review and revise any of his own previous directions,

(xii) Conduct the Adjudication inquisitorially, and take the initiative in ascertaining the facts and the law,

(xiii) Reach his decision with or without holding an oral hearing, and with or without having endeavoured to facilitate an agreement between the Parties.

20. The Adjudicator shall exercise such powers with a view of fairness and impartiality, giving each Party a reasonable opportunity, in light of the timetable, of putting his case and dealing with that of his opponents.

21. The Adjudicator may not

(i) Require any advance payment of or security for his fees

(ii) Receive any written submissions from one Party that are not also made available to the others

(iii) Refuse any Party the right at any hearing or meeting to be represented by any representative of that Party's choosing who is present

(iv) Act or continue to act in the face of a conflict of interest

(v) Require any Party to pay or make contribution to the legal costs of another Party arising in the Adjudication.

22. The Adjudicator shall reach a decision within 28 days of referral or such longer period as is agreed by the Parties after the dispute has been referred to him. The Adjudicator shall be entitled to extend the said period of 28 days by up to 14 days with the consent of the Party by whom the dispute was referred.

Adjudicator's Fees and Expenses

23.   If a Party shall request Adjudication, and it is subsequently established that he is not entitled to do so, that Party shall be solely responsible for the Adjudicator's fees and expenses.

24.   Save as aforesaid, the Parties shall be jointly responsible for the Adjudicator's fees and expenses including those of any specialist consultant appointed under 19(viii). In his decision, the Adjudicator shall have the discretion to make directions with regard to those fees and expenses. If no such directions are made, the Parties shall bear such fees and expenses in equal shares, and if any Party has paid more than such equal share, that Party shall be entitled to contribution from other Parties accordingly.

25.   The Adjudicator's fees shall not exceed the rate of £1000 per day or part day, plus expenses and VAT.

Decisions

26.   The Adjudicator may in any decision direct the payment of such compound or simple interest as may be commercially reasonable.

27.   All decisions shall be in writing, but shall not include any reasons.

Enforcement

28.   Every decision of the Adjudicator shall be implemented without delay. The Parties shall be entitled to such reliefs and remedies as are set out in the decision, and shall be entitled to summary enforcement thereof, regardless of whether such decision is or is to be the subject of any challenge or review. No party shall be entitled to raise any right of set-off, counterclaim or abatement in connection with any enforcement proceedings.

Immunity, Confidentiality and Non-Compellability

29.   Neither ORSA, nor its Chairman, nor deputy, nor the Adjudicator nor any employee or agent of any of them shall be liable for anything done or not done in the discharge or purported discharge of his functions as Adjudicator, whether in negligence or otherwise, unless the act or omission is in bad faith.

30.   The Adjudication and all matters arising in the course thereof are and will be kept confidential by the Parties except insofar as necessary to implement or enforce any decision of the Adjudicator or as may be required for the purpose of any subsequent proceedings.

31.   In the event that any Party seeks to challenge or review any decision of the Adjudicator in any subsequent litigation or arbitration, the Adjudicator shall not be joined as a party to, nor shall be subpoenaed or otherwise to give evidence or provide his notes in such litigation or arbitration.

Law

32.   These Rules shall be governed by English law and under the jurisdiction of the English Courts.

33.   No Party shall, save in case of bad faith on the part of the Adjudicator, make any application to the courts whatsoever in relation to the conduct of the Adjudication or the decision of the Adjudicator until such time as the Adjudicator has made his decision, or refused to make a decision, and until the Party making the application has complied with any such decision.

Appendix 6 Brief explanations of "set-off" and "abatement"

There are a number of recognised categories of set-off which are governed by principles established in the leading case of *Hanak* v *Green* [1958 2 QB 9, 2 All ER 141], which are:

A set-off of mutual liquidated debts

The set-off is a cross-claim which is known, or can be ascertained, with certainty. This category of set-off is available where the claims on both sides are in respect of liquidated debts. If the debt cannot be ascertained with certainty without a decision of a court or an arbitrator it cannot be applied as a set-off, subject to the other categories of set-off.

Equitable set-off

An equitable set-off applies in circumstances where the cross-claim is so closely connected with the claim that to disallow the set-off would produce a manifestly unjust result. Liquidated damages not exceeding the amount of the claim and arising under the same contract can normally be set-off against the claim.

Abatement

The remedy of abatement only applies to breaches of warranty for contract for sale of goods and for work and labour. The essence of abatement concerns the value of the work and materials, thus the measure of abatement is *"how much less the subject matter of the action [is] worth by reason of the breach"* (*Mondel* v *Steel* 1841 8M&W 858 at 871)

Additionally there are two other categories:

Contractual set-off

Some of the standard forms of contract make provision for set-off, although in many situations a legal or equitable set-off is available as of right.

Subject to establishing an equitable set-off, one party is not able to set-off claims arising under one contract against another unconnected contract. The parties can however extend the entitlement to set-off in a contract by providing for a claim arising under that contract to be set-off against another unconnected contract.

Statutory set-off

Rights of set-off can arise under statute as, for example under the Insolvency Act 1986.

References for more information:

Derham R. *Set-off*. Oxford University Press, second edition, 1996.

Jones N.F. Set-off in the construction industry. *Construction Law Journal*, Vol 7, No 2, pp 84–101, 1991.

References

1 *The placing and management of contracts for building and civil engineering work: Report of the Banwell Committee.* Ministry of Public Building and Works, 1964.

2 *The placing and management of building contracts: Report of the Central Council for Works and Buildings.* Chaired by E. D. Simon. Ministry of Works, 1944.

3 Sir Michael Latham. *Constructing the team.* HMSO, London, 1994.

4 Joyce, R. *The Construction (Design and Management) Regulations 1994 explained.* Thomas Telford, London, 1995.

5 *A. Cameron Limited* v *John Mowlem & Company plc.* 25 Con LR11, 52 Build LR24.

6 *Making the Scheme for Construction Contracts.* A consultation document issued by the Department of the Environment. November 1996.

7 The Housing Grants, Construction and Regeneration Act 1996 (Commencement No 1) Order (SI 1996:2352).

8 *The Supreme Court Practice 1995.* Sweet and Maxwell.

9 *The County Court Practice 1996.* Butterworth.